980

D1263943

*An Introduction to*

# NONLINEAR OPTICS

*An Introduction to*

# NONLINEAR OPTICS

## George C. Baldwin

*Professor of Applied Physics*
*Division of Nuclear Engineering and Science*
*Rensselaer Polytechnic Institute*
*Troy, New York*

PLENUM PRESS • NEW YORK • 1969

*Library of Congress Catalog Card Number 69-16517*

© 1969 Plenum Press
A Division of Plenum Publishing Corporation
227 West 17 Street, New York, New York 10011

Printed in the United States of America

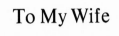

To My Wife

# FOREWORD

Many years spent in an industrial engineering laboratory have convinced me that there is ever-increasing need to present recent and current research in forms which can be easily assimilated by engineers, technical managers, and others concerned with applications and the development of new technology. There is a forbidding gap between the typical research paper, addressed by specialists to other specialists, and the popular-level account addressed to the layman. The second does not adequately prepare the engineer for profitably studying the first; it does not impart sufficient depth of understanding to the manager who must make decisions on the relative merits of various approaches to a problem or on the potential contributions various specialists might make to his program.

This book is the outgrowth of a review prepared to fill this need for engineers in a large corporation who were concerned with the industrial application of lasers. That review was written hurriedly, on a fixed budget, to a deadline; consequently, it contained oversimplifications and errors, not all of which were trivial. Nevertheless, the favorable response proved that such a review is indeed needed. It is hoped that this more finished work will prove useful to a wide variety of potential users of laser-centered devices and systems, and may even stimulate the generation of useful ideas.

One problem encountered in this undertaking is that of giving personal recognition to the great many individuals who have contributed to the development of nonlinear optics. To maintain the emphasis on the phenomena and on the underlying mechanisms, one must minimize the number of personal references. Rather than single out a few outstanding contributors, perhaps inadvertently and unjustly omitting others whose contributions were equally significant, I have chosen to omit names entirely from the text after the second chapter. This omission is partially compensated by an extensive, but by no means comprehensive, bibliography.

Lastly, there have been many individuals, also nameless here although greatly appreciated, who helped in various ways in developing my understanding and in transferring it to the manuscript.

# CONTENTS

# 1.

# INTRODUCTION

## 1.1. THE SCOPE OF OPTICS

Optics is the branch of physical science which describes the generation, composition, transmission, and interactions of light, and endeavors to relate these to other physical phenomena.

Put more precisely, the subject matter of optics concerns the propagation and interactions of electromagnetic waves with matter, not only in that part of their frequency spectrum in which they actually produce visual sensation, but also in adjacent regions of the spectrum, within which they have similar properties and so can be studied with similar techniques.

The electromagnetic spectrum is shown in Figure 1. It can be seen that the strictly visual range is confined to one octave, while the extended range which comprises the subject matter of optics is about one decade.

The study of light and its properties has proved to be richly rewarding, both to science and to technology. It affords an outstanding example of the power of scientific methods. Optical instruments have vastly extended the

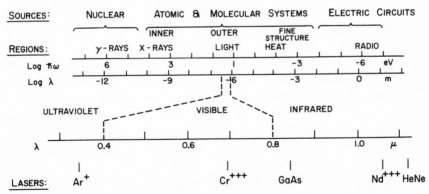

Figure 1. The electromagnetic radiation spectrum, showing the wavelength region of interest to optics and some of the laser sources which have been useful for research in nonlinear optics.

range of human vision. Long before space travel was possible, the telescope and later the spectroscope made man aware of the existence of other worlds, and thus increased his understanding of his own. The finite velocity of light was first revealed with the telescope. The microscope and the spectroscope enabled scientists to probe the inner structure of matter. Photography greatly multiplied the resolution of these and other instruments and revealed the existence of new kinds of light not perceptible to that remarkable but limited instrument, the human eye; this provided superior probes for the study of matter. Moreover, photography revolutionized communication, making possible the wide dissemination of knowledge and understanding so essential in a world rapidly shrinking in the wake of scientific and engineering progress.

## 1.2. HISTORICAL BACKGROUND

The question of the nature of light was an outstanding problem in the early days of modern physical science. Some scientists were inclined to doubt that light could pass through a perfect vacuum. Others could not understand how it could pass through matter. That something had to propagate at a definite velocity from source to observer was proved by Roemer's astronomical observations, but the phenomena of refraction and dispersion studied carefully by Newton and Huyghens could be explained equally well by either corpuscular or wave hypotheses. To Newton, the lack of any evidence of diffraction was proof that light can not be a wave. The opponents of his corpuscular hypothesis, led by Huyghens, were impressed by the transparency of many dense media and by the lack of any evidence for interaction between two light beams which traverse the same portion of a medium simultaneously. These properties are characteristic of waves, as one may readily verify by observing ripples on the surface of water or noting that, though one may be exposed simultaneously to sounds from a variety of sources, it is ordinarily possible to distinguish them, provided they are not too intense.

Young's discovery of the interference of light, made early in the nineteenth century, seemed to settle the controversy. The magnitude of the wavelength proved to be extremely short compared to the sizes of typical macroscopic objects; thus rectilinear propagation was explained. Color proved to be related to wavelength or frequency.

These facts provided a basis for a quantitative theory of light waves analogous to that of elastic vibrations in solids, which sufficed to account for all the optical phenomena then observed. This theory was further sustained by measurement of the velocity of light by Fresnel and Fizeau, which showed that light propagates at lower velocity in a transparent medium than in vacuum; this effect is opposite to that which Newton had required to explain the refraction of a beam of corpuscles.

The nature of the wave phenomenon itself and of the medium which supports it remained a mystery until Maxwell conceived the possibility of electromagnetic waves and showed that their velocity *in vacuo* should be precisely equal to the measured velocity of light. Hertz confirmed Maxwell's theory by demonstrating the reality of much longer electromagnetic waves radiated from electrical circuits and showing their qualitative similarity to light. At about the same time, the Michelson–Morley experiment shattered the concept of an all-pervading solid medium in which the elastic vibrations of Fresnel's theory could be supported.

The recognition that light is an electromagnetic wave was one of the great milestones of scientific thought, since it unified the description of a great diversity of phenomena, enabled scientists to predict with confidence the existence and properties of previously unknown forms of electromagnetic radiation, and made it possible to understand the optical properties of matter. The transparency of some substances and the opacity of others, the mysterious phenomena of absorption and refraction, yielded to a unified theory of dispersion developed by Rayleigh, Drude, and Lorentz which related the optical properties of a substance to its electrical properties. This was accomplished by postulating an internal electrical structure for the atom and calculating its response to impressed electromagnetic fields of various frequencies. By 1890, the rapid progress and astonishing success of the electromagnetic theory of light seemed to many to be a sign that the task of fundamental science was nearing completion. Their complacency was soon shattered. The failure of classical theory to explain the spectrum of radiation from incandescent substances, followed in rapid succession by the discoveries of the photoelectric effect, X rays, radioactivity, and the combination principle of atomic spectra, confronted physicists with paradoxes. Planck and Einstein showed that these anomalies could be resolved only by reviving the corpuscular hypothesis; now, however, this had to be done in a way which could be reconciled with the firmly established wave theory of light.

Modern quantum theory is the result of this synthesis. So long as one's concern is solely with the propagation of light, it is permissible to represent it as a classical electromagnetic wave in which the field intensities are continuous functions of space and time. In any interactions of the wave fields with matter, however, it is the exchanges of energy and momentum which account for the observable effects, and the experimental evidence is overwhelming that these exchanges are not continuous; they occur only in discrete steps (or multiples thereof) of magnitude proportional to the frequency of the wave field. Even at visible frequencies, of the order of $10^{15}$ sec$^{-1}$, each quantum step is so minute that a vast number of individual quantum exchanges will be involved in the transfer of even minute amounts of energy. This has led to a widely favored interpretation that the electromagnetic wave is truly corpuscular, and that the field intensities in the wave merely express probabilities for the presence of energy quanta or "photons." On this interpretation, the coefficients of interaction (which relate the field intensities of the wave to physical effects which it creates when passing through matter) are probabilities for the transfer of energy quanta from the wave field to the matter. The work of DeBroglie, Schrödinger, Heisenberg, and many others during the first half of the twentieth century led to the development of a highly sophisticated mathematical structure for assessing these transition probabilities. Despite its elegance of formal structure, classical dispersion theory was unable to predict the numerical values of the interaction coefficients and the characteristic frequencies, a task in which quantum mechanics has been remarkably successful.

There are strong misgivings in some quarters, however, because quantum mechanics consists principally of rules of computation, the justification for which rests mainly on their success, rather than on an underlying physical content. There is general agreement that quantum mechanics is correct as a mathematical system, but its physical basis is, to many, obscure.

With the quantum theory firmly established, at least as a computational artifice, optics once again seemed a "complete" science: the attention of physicists turned from the nature of light itself to the fine structure of matter, to the interaction of electromagnetic radiation with matter at frequencies far removed from the optical range, and with the fundamental particles. Again optics awaited developments in another field of investigation. These have come within the past decade. Optics is once again an active research field, yielding deeper insights into the structure of matter.

## 1.3. LINEARITY IN OPTICS

In comparison with other branches of physics, optics seemed to make rapid progress. This could be attributed to several factors. Visual optics deals with readily perceived phenomena, and the adjacent spectral regions are accessible to similar techniques of detection and measurement. The quantum unit and the wavelength of visible light are both so small that the fields of the wave may be represented accurately by continuous functions and its propagation can usually be described to sufficient accuracy by geometrical optics, the approximation in which diffraction is unimportant and only the direction of energy transport is of concern. Moreover, even when wave structure must be considered, the theoretical framework is relatively simple; the basic equations of electromagnetic wave propagation are linear in all commonly encountered circumstances. The linear nature of these equations greatly simplifies the character of their wave solutions. The sum of two or more solutions of a linear differential wave equation is also a solution, and so is any linear combination of its solutions. This is the principle of superposition; it accounts for the early observation, noted above, that two light waves do not appear to modify or scatter each other when they are made to intersect in an optical medium.

These characteristics made it possible for scientific understanding of optics to develop in discrete stages, each one of which really was only an approximation, but a very good one. Each sufficed until refinements in observational technique or an insight from another discipline led to the next stage of understanding.

Recent research in optics has shown that the linearity of the wave equations in optical media is only an approximation, albeit a very good one. The coefficients of the nonlinear terms are extremely small, but under proper circumstances, they lead to striking effects. The existence, character, and magnitudes of these nonlinearities provide more detailed information about the structure of matter and promise dividends to technology. These developments, while fundamental, are found to confirm, clarify, and extend, rather than to upset, the established theories of optical interaction.

Among newly observed effects which call for new refinements in optical theory are the amplification of light, the mixing of light waves to create new frequencies, spectral changes in beams of light passed through normally transparent media, the generation of sound waves by light, which is spectrally changed in the process, and the ionization of atoms by visual or even infrared light.

## 1.4. NONLINEARITY IN OTHER FIELDS

The simplicity which linearity conferred to the development of optics contrasts sharply with the complexity of electronics. There a rich variety of phenomena arising from nonlinear responses of vacuum tubes, diodes, transistors, saturable reactors, etc. have been exploited to create a diversity of both general and specialized technologies for the transmission and processing of information, the monitoring and control of complex processes and systems, and the generation and conversion of electrical energy. In many of these phenomena (e.g., rectification, inversion, modulation, harmonic generation, heterodyning, to name a few), nonlinearity is the essential property of the element.

Nonlinear effects are also well-known in acoustics, particularly to the high-fidelity enthusiast. Intermodulation distortion, his *bête noire*, is a consequence of frequency mixing by a nonlinear characteristic of his pickup, amplifier, or speaker. If he raises the volume sufficiently, he becomes aware of additional intermodulation, some of which may be created within his ear by its nonlinear response to beats between notes of different frequency. As the latter will be perceived also within the concert hall, he finds its "realism" pleasing; he is greatly distressed by similar nonlinearity in his equipment.

## 1.5. NONLINEARITY IN OPTICS

The foundation for nonlinear optics was laid gradually during the long period in which the electromagnetic theory of light, the electron theory of dispersion, and, finally, the quantum theory were established. A number of interesting optical effects were discovered during this period. The remarkable phenomena of double refraction and optical activity were explained in terms of anisotropic binding of the dispersion electrons to the crystal unit cell or molecule, and were recognized as useful tools for the identification of minerals and the investigation of crystal structure.

The discovery that strong electric fields can induce double refraction in normally isotropic media (Kerr and Pockels electrooptical effects) was also easily explained as evidence of distortion of the unit cell structure which contrains the dispersion electrons within the crystal lattice. Magnetooptical effects were also discovered. The Zeeman effect, in which spectral lines were split by a magnetic field, was explained with partial success in classical terms as a combination of the frequency of the impressed light wave with the frequency of Larmor precession of the electrons in the applied magnetic field. In combination with dispersion theory, this provided a basis for explaining the double refraction which is induced by magnetic fields (Cotton–Mouton and Faraday effects). Full quantitative explanation of these effects required quantum-theoretical methods, however. A similar but more involved problem was presented by the Raman effect; there the response of the optical medium is not simply passive refraction; it involves addition to the wave of new frequencies characteristic, not simply of the electron motion, but of mechanical vibration in the molecular structure. This effect cannot occur in a linear medium.

Optical nonlinearity is manifested by changes in the optical properties of a medium as the intensity of the impressed light wave is increased or when one or more other light waves are introduced.

Two general categories of optical nonlinearity can be recognized at once. We shall use the terms extrinsic and intrinsic to distinguish them.

*Extrinsic nonlinearity* is a change of properties which is directly related to changes of the composition of the medium which result from absorption or emission of light. Such change may be in the relative populations of ground and excited states or in the numbers of optically effective electrons. Certain dyes widely used for laser $Q$-switching, the laser medium itself, and laser mirrors coated with semiconductors have this property. The history of exposure as well as the instantaneous intensity of the light determines their optical behavior.

*Intrinsic nonlinear* optical phenomena which we shall describe are violations of the principle of superposition, arising from nonlinear response of the individual molecule or unit cell to the fields of two or more light waves. This category includes nonlinear response to a single light beam, since it is permissible to regard any light beam as a summation of two or more similar light waves identical in polarization, frequency, and direction.

In either type of nonlinearity, the optical properties of the medium depend on the intensity of the light, and it is useful to classify them according to the power of the intensity involved. For example, the intensity of the second-harmonic light at $\lambda = 0.53\ \mu$ generated in lithium niobate by radiation from a neodymium laser is observed to be proportional to the square of the intensity of the 1.06-$\mu$ fundamental, and this is therefore classified as a second-order nonlinear process. Some nonlinear optical effects include:

| | |
|---|---|
| Second-harmonic scattering | (2). |
| Rectification | (2). |
| Sum-and-difference frequency generation | (2). |
| Third-harmonic scattering | (3). |
| Raman scattering | (2). |
| Brillouin scattering | (2). |
| Inverse Raman effect | (2). |
| Inverse Faraday effect | (3). |
| Two-photon absorption | (2). |
| Intensity-dependent refraction | (2, 3). |
| Induced opacity | (2). |
| Induced reflectivity | (2). |
| Breakdown of gases | ($N$). |

The respective orders of nonlinearity are designated by the numbers in parenthesis which follow each item. Further details must await the detailed account in later sections.

As in the case of the Pockels effect, these phenomena demonstrate nonlinear distortions of the electrical structure of the medium. Here the applied fields are time-varying vector quantities; the effects they produce depend not only on intensity, but also upon the directions of propagation and polarization and on the phase relationships among the several interacting light waves.

Each transition to the next stage in the development of optics involved the development of advanced technology as well as of concepts. To establish the wave theory required the observation of extremely fine detail in diffraction patterns and the ability to produce gratings, lenses, etc., of good quality. Quantum theory rests largely on the highly precise and sensitive techniques of spectroscopy. Similarly, the observation of nonlinear optical phenomena had to await new technology.

The electric field intensities in typical light waves are not particularly strong. In bright sunshine, for example, the amplitude of the electric intensity is about 600 V/m, far less than the electric intensity of 5(11) V/m which binds the dispersion electron in a hydrogen atom. Because of the great disparity of these magnitudes, it was taken for granted that nonlinearity would never be important in optics, despite the evidence of the electro-optical and magnetooptical effects.

The key which opened the door to nonlinear optics was the development of the maser by Townes and his co-workers in this country and by Basov and Prokhovov in the USSR. This device employs stimulated emission to generate narrowband microwave radiation from a properly prepared medium. The success of the maser led to attempts to develop an optical-frequency analog. The resulting family of lasers now numbers hundreds of varieties, distinguished by the nature of the active medium, operating wavelength, energy input mechanism or pump, time cycle, and intensity. They produce highly monochromatic beams of light which can be concentrated to extremely high intensities.

A peculiar property of the laser beam, essential to nonlinear optics, is its high degree of coherence. Ordinary light consists of the resultant of uncorrelated contributions to the wave field from an enormous number of independently radiating atomic systems. Because of this, ordinary light is not coherent, i.e., well-defined phase relationships do not persist among the wave fields observed at different points of time or space. Laser radiation, on the other hand, is highly coherent, because the simulated emissions of different radiating atoms are synchronized.

Coherence enables one to concentrate the radiation by focusing a laser beam onto a small area, the minimum size of which is limited only by diffraction and by the optical quality of the laser and the focusing system. It is possible in this way to obtain extremely intense local radiation fields, but in small volumes.

Coherence also enables one to combine the weak contributions of nonlinear interactions from widely separated parts of an extended medium so as to produce an appreciable resultant. With ordinary, incoherent light, both approaches are limited, and it is possible to observe many interesting nonlinear optical phenomena only with the aid of laser sources.

## 1.6. SCOPE OF THIS BOOK

This book is intended as an introduction to the subject rather than as a treatise or textbook. Its purpose is to review nonlinear optics by description and explanations which strive for simplicity, brevity, and clarity rather than for completeness and rigor. It is directed toward the engineer or scientist whose specialty leaves little time for study in depth, but who is interested in keeping informed of other fields or, having reason to suspect that new developments in optics may have significance for his work, needs a relatively elementary but nonetheless thorough account before he attacks the rather formidable literature.

For such readers, simple classical models are desirable, and we shall employ them wherever possible; however, the interaction of light with matter obviously cannot be adequately described without the aid of quantum mechanics.

Since nonlinear effects in optics arise from small perturbations, it is logical to develop the subject by first reviewing the framework of linear optics and then showing how the nonlinear phenomena appear upon introducing additional refinements into the theory. The experimental observations will then be introduced as required to illustrate and confirm the theoretical exposition. A bibliography appears at the end of the text for those who wish to pursue the subject further, and a mathematical appendix has been included for those who need to be reminded of the effect of nonlinearity.

A second reason for first reviewing the field of linear optics is to establish a single, consistent framework of concepts, units, and nomenclature. This is especially needed in respect to units. Much of the data in the literature appear in cgs units; nevertheless, engineers and many physicists have found that consistent use of the mks system for electrical and mechanical quantities eliminates much of the tedious and risky arithmetical labor of conversion. The choice of mks units in this book is deliberate, and is made with a plea for their wider use. They lend themselves better to dimensional reasoning, and their use eliminates an annoying source of confusion and error.

# 2.

# BACKGROUND OF NONLINEAR OPTICS

## 2.1. ELECTROMAGNETIC THEORY OF LIGHT

### 2.1.1. Fields and Inductions. The electromagnetic theory of light
is implicit in the relationships, known as Maxwell's equations, among associated electric and magnetic fields. The measures of these fields, termed intensities and inductions, are vector functions of space and time. Their physical significance is often a source of confusion.

The field intensities $\mathbf{E}$ and $\mathbf{H}$ are commonly defined in terms of the forces which would be experienced by a small, unit test charge or a free, unit magnetic pole if it could be placed at the given point without significantly disturbing the field. Free charges do exist, particularly as electrons or ions, bearing positive or negative multiples of the electron charge, $e = -1.602(-19)$ C.* Since $e$ is a very small quantity, the definition of $\mathbf{E}$ has some operational significance.

Magnetic test entities, on the other hand, exist only in the form of dipoles associated with motion, circulation, or rotation of electric charges, so that this kind of test cannot be performed for magnetic fields, and alternative definitions for $\mathbf{H}$ are preferable.

We shall define both electric and magnetic quantities in terms of the force on a unit test charge, using the single equation

$$\mathbf{F} = e(\mathbf{E} + \mathbf{v} \times \mathbf{B}), \tag{1}$$

in which $\mathbf{v}$ is the velocity of the test charge and $\mathbf{B}$ is the magnetic induction. The electric field $\mathbf{E}$ is measured by a stationary test charge; the magnetic induction contributes an additional, velocity-dependent force on moving charges.

---

* The number in parentheses is the power of ten by which the numerical coefficient is to be multiplied; in this case, $1.602(-19) \equiv 1.602 \times 10^{-19}$.

The unit of $\mathbf{E}$ is the newton per coulomb, or its equivalent, the joule meter$^{-1}$ coulomb$^{-1}$, which is usually abbreviated as the volt per meter.

The magnetic induction is equal in magnitude to the force exerted on a unit test charge, in the absence of an electric field, as it traverses the field point at unit velocity. The unit of $\mathbf{B}$ is the newton meter$^{-1}$ coulomb$^{-1}$ second, usually abbreviated volt second meter$^{-2}$.

The electric field intensity $\mathbf{E}$ results, in general, not only from free charges, either in space or placed on isolated material bodies, but also from electric dipoles and multipoles of higher order, and, in particular, from dipoles which it causes to appear, either by displacing bound charges or by reorienting permanent electric dipoles in matter. Electric field lines, of density and direction given by $\mathbf{E}$, begin on positive charges and terminate on negative charges, regardless of whether these charges are bound or free. It is useful to employ the concept of lines of electric induction which begin and end only on the primary sources of the field. In the rationalized mks system, the electric induction $\mathbf{D}$ is measured in coulombs per square meter, in agreement with Gauss' law, which states that the total number of lines of induction passing through a closed surface is numerically equal to the net free charge contained within it. Like weight and mass, $\mathbf{D}$ and $\mathbf{E}$ have different physical dimensions.

In empty space, the electric field intensity $\mathbf{E}$ is everywhere directly proportional to the electric induction. This fact is usually written

$$\mathbf{D} = \varepsilon_0 \mathbf{E}. \tag{2}$$

The coefficient of proportionality $\varepsilon_0$ has the dimensions coulomb volt$^{-1}$ meter$^{-1}$. The various modifications of this simple relationship introduced by the presence of polarizable matter are the basis, not only of electrostatics, but also of optics.

To complete the description of an electromagnetic field, it is necessary to relate $\mathbf{B}$ to its sources. The magnetic quantity analogous to $\mathbf{D}$ is the field intensity $\mathbf{H}$, measured in ampere (turns) per meter. Note that only steady circulating currents can give rise to steady magnetic fields. The proportionality corresponding to Eq. (2) for magnetic fields in vacuum is

$$\mathbf{B} = \mu_0 \mathbf{H}. \tag{3}$$

In those material media which contain permanent magnetic dipoles (atomic current loops or unpaired electron spins), a more complicated relationship will exist.

Unlike $\varepsilon_0$, $\mu_0$ need not be experimentally determined, since the ampere, and hence the coulomb, can be defined if one chooses to assign a particular value to $\mu_0$. By convention, this value is $4\pi(-7)$ V-sec/A-m. This convention of the mks system which reverses the order of defining the units of charge or current and of the various measures of the field is practically convenient, but is widely regarded as pedagogically inconvenient, hence the persistence of the cgs system with its fictitious magnetic poles, despite the labor of conversion it entails whenever one must deal with practical quantities.

Note that the quantities $\mathbf{D} \cdot \mathbf{E}/2$ and $\mathbf{B} \cdot \mathbf{H}/2$ both have dimensions J/m³; the value of

$$U = \tfrac{1}{2}(\mathbf{D} \cdot \mathbf{E} + \mathbf{B} \cdot \mathbf{H})\, \varDelta V \qquad (4)$$

in a small volume element $\varDelta V$ in the field represents its share of the total work done in establishing the field configuration. This energy resides in the electromagnetic field, and will be transported from that region to another whenever the local field is changed.

### 2.1.2. Maxwell's Equations. 
The associations among time-varying electric and magnetic field quantities are more involved than those for steady fields. Steady electric fields originate from the presence of charge, and magnetic fields from the sustained motion of electric charge; either kind of field can also be induced by changes in the other kind. The complete relationships are contained in the four differential equations of Maxwell:

$$\nabla \cdot \mathbf{D} = \varrho, \qquad (5)$$

$$\nabla \cdot \mathbf{B} = 0, \qquad (6)$$

$$\nabla \times \mathbf{E} = -\dot{\mathbf{B}}, \qquad (7)$$

$$\nabla \times \mathbf{H} = \dot{\mathbf{D}} + \mathbf{J}. \qquad (8)$$

The first two are differential forms of Gauss' law and are essentially geometrical identities. Equation (5) contains the inverse-square law for the field of a point charge; Eq. (6) also contains the assertion that free magnetic poles do not exist.

The third Maxwell equation is the differential form of Faraday's law of induction; the reader may verify this by integrating each side of Eq. (7) over a surface and applying Stokes' theorem to convert the left side to a line integral about the perimeter of that surface.

The last equation contains Ampere's law, but with the important additional statement that magnetic fields arise, not only from actually circulating electric charges, of density **J** amperes per square meter, but also from time variations in the electric displacement **D**. It is this phenomenon of "displacement currents" which gives rise to electromagnetic waves, and so, to light.

Definition of **E** and **B** by Eq. (1) implies a particular frame of reference in which the velocity of the test charge is determined. Two observers in relative motion will therefore not obtain the same set of values for **E** and **B**.

The close interrelationship of the field variables suggests the possibility of representing an electromagnetic field by means of a single field variable. Although this cannot be done, alternative representations exist which are more useful for certain kinds of problems. The scalar and vector potentials, $\phi$ and **A**, are particularly convenient concepts in making the transition to quantum theory. They are related to the field variables by

$$\mathbf{E} = \dot{\mathbf{A}} + \boldsymbol{\nabla}\phi, \tag{9}$$

$$\mathbf{B} = \boldsymbol{\nabla} \times \mathbf{A}. \tag{10}$$

This representation is also not unique, depending on the frame of reference.

### 2.1.3. Plane Electromagnetic Waves in Vacuum.
In space containing no free charges, the quantities $\varrho$ and **J** vanish from the right-hand sides of Eqs. (5) and (8). The two equations of electromagnetic induction then combine into a single relation applicable to either the electric or the magnetic intensity. For instance, substituting Eq. (4) into Eq. (7), taking the curl of both sides, and combining with Eq. (8), one eliminates **H** and obtains the propagation equation for the electric vector:

$$\boldsymbol{\nabla} \times (\boldsymbol{\nabla} \times \mathbf{E}) + \varepsilon_0\mu_0\ddot{\mathbf{E}} = 0. \tag{11}$$

Similarly, by substituting Eq. (2) into Eq. (8) and taking the curl as before, one finds an exactly similar equation for **H**:

$$\boldsymbol{\nabla} \times (\boldsymbol{\nabla} \times \mathbf{H}) + \varepsilon_0\mu_0\ddot{\mathbf{H}} = 0. \tag{12}$$

By using Eqs. (5) and (6) and a well-known vector identity, these simplify to the familiar mathematical form of the equation of wave propagation:

$$c^2 \boldsymbol{\nabla}^2\mathbf{E} = \partial^2\mathbf{E}/\partial t^2, \tag{13}$$

$$c^2 \boldsymbol{\nabla}^2\mathbf{H} = \partial^2\mathbf{H}/\partial t^2. \tag{14}$$

Equations (11) and (12) describe wave propagation of the vector quantities

**E** and **H** at the velocity

$$c = (\varepsilon_0 \mu_0)^{-1/2}. \tag{15}$$

Any function of the form $f(\mathbf{r} \pm ct)$, where $\mathbf{r}$ is a space coordinate, will satisfy the propagation equations. In particular, the wave equations admit solutions

$$\mathbf{E} = \mathbf{E}_0 \cos\{\omega_0 t - \mathbf{k}_0 \cdot \mathbf{r}\} \tag{16}$$

and

$$\mathbf{H} = \mathbf{H}_0 \cos\{\omega_0 t - \mathbf{k}_0 \cdot \mathbf{r}\}, \tag{17}$$

simple harmonic plane waves in which the phase of the field vector propagates at a constant velocity $\omega_0/k_0$ in the direction specified by the vector $\mathbf{k}_0$. At any instant, the fields at two points $\mathbf{r}, \mathbf{r}'$ differ in phase by $\mathbf{k}_0 \cdot (\mathbf{r} - \mathbf{r}')$; the wavelength is therefore $2\pi/k_0$.

Applying the space and time differentiations* indicated in the field equations to these solutions,

$$\nabla \times \mathbf{E} = \mathbf{k}_0 \times \mathbf{E}_0 \sin\{\omega_0 t - \mathbf{k}_0 \cdot \mathbf{r}\}, \tag{18}$$

$$\dot{\mathbf{B}} = -\mu_0 \omega_0 \mathbf{H}_0 \sin\{\omega_0 t - \mathbf{k}_0 \cdot \mathbf{r}\}, \tag{19}$$

$$\nabla \times \mathbf{H} = \mathbf{k}_0 \times \mathbf{H}_0 \sin\{\omega_0 t - \mathbf{k}_0 \cdot \mathbf{r}\}, \tag{20}$$

$$\dot{\mathbf{D}} = -\varepsilon_0 \omega_0 \mathbf{E}_0 \sin\{\omega_0 t - \mathbf{k}_0 \cdot \mathbf{r}\}, \tag{21}$$

we find that they are equivalent to the following constant relationships:

$$\mathbf{k}_0 \times \mathbf{E}_0 = \mu_0 \omega_0 \mathbf{H}_0, \tag{22}$$

$$\mathbf{k}_0 \times \mathbf{H}_0 = -\varepsilon_0 \omega_0 \mathbf{E}_0. \tag{23}$$

These show that the propagation vector $\mathbf{k}_0$ is perpendicular to the plane containing the directions of **E** and **H**, i.e., the wave is transverse and plane-polarized (Figure 2). The magnitudes of **E** and **H** bear the ratio

---

* To perform the space differentiation, use the vector identity

$$\nabla \times (\phi \mathbf{E}_0) = \nabla\phi \times \mathbf{E}_0 + \phi \nabla \times \mathbf{E}_0$$

and represent the cosine function by $\phi$. Then, taking the gradient

$$\nabla[\cos\{\omega t - \mathbf{k}_0 \cdot \mathbf{r}\}] = -k_0 \sin\{\omega t - \mathbf{k}_0 \cdot \mathbf{r}\}$$

and noting that $E_0$ is a constant vector, we obtain the result of Eq. (18).

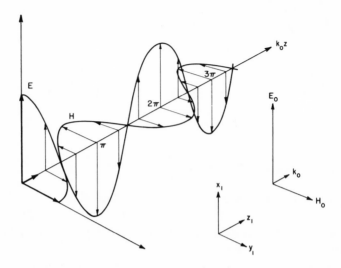

Figure 2. A plane-polarized electromagnetic wave. The sinusoidal
curves represent the instantaneous magnitudes and directions of
the electric and magnetic fields at various distances along the
direction of wave propagation.

$(\mu_0/\varepsilon_0)^{1/2}$. The phase velocity is

$$c = \omega_0/k_0 = (\varepsilon_0\mu_0)^{-1/2}. \tag{24}$$

Each (electric, magnetic) wave may be regarded as creating its associated
(magnetic, electric) wave by electromagnetic induction. Note that $\mathbf{E} \cdot \mathbf{D}$
$= \mathbf{B} \cdot \mathbf{H}$, so that energy is shared equally by electric and magnetic fields.

It is algebraically convenient to employ exponential rather than trigonometric functions to describe a harmonic wave. The exponential form equivalent to Eq. (16) is

$$\mathbf{E} = (\mathbf{E}_0/2) \exp i\{\omega_0 t - \mathbf{k}_0 \cdot \mathbf{r}\} + \overline{(\mathbf{E}_0/2)} \exp i\{\mathbf{k}_0 \cdot \mathbf{r} - \omega_0 t\}. \tag{25}$$

When a phase shift should be included in the argument of the trigonometric
wave, the corresponding exponential form has complex amplitude. The bar
above the amplitude factor will denote the complex conjugate.

One often finds the first term of (25) alone, without the factor of $\frac{1}{2}$,
and with the understanding that the actual physical wave corresponds only
to the real part of the complex exponential function. The absence of the
factor of $\frac{1}{2}$ leads to confusion. *The exponential notation, when used herein,
will always imply addition of the complex conjugate*, as shown above, and
we shall include the factor of $\frac{1}{2}$.

## 2.1.4. Energy Flow from Sources to Sinks. Any electromagnetic wave is a carrier of energy. It must originate somewhere in the motion of an electric charge distribution, and must eventually be manifested by its effects on the motion of other distant charges or charge distributions.

The rate at which energy is transported by an electromagnetic wave across a surface element **da** is given by

$$\mathbf{S} \cdot \mathbf{da} \quad \text{watts,} \tag{26}$$

where the quantity

$$\mathbf{S} = \mathbf{E} \times \mathbf{H} \quad \text{watts per square meter} \tag{27}$$

is called the Poynting vector. For the plane wave of Eqs. (16) and (17), it has the particular value

$$\mathbf{S} = (\mathbf{E}_0 \times \mathbf{H}_0) \cos^2\{\omega_0 t - \mathbf{k}_0 \cdot \mathbf{r}\}, \tag{28}$$

$$\mathbf{S} = \mathbf{k}_0 (E_0{}^2/\mu_0 \omega_0) \cos^2\{\omega_0 t - \mathbf{k}_0 \cdot \mathbf{r}\}, \tag{29}$$

the second form following from Eqs. (22) and (23) and the vector identity for the triple vector product.

Thus, energy always flows in the direction of propagation of the wave, with the time average value

$$S_{\text{avg}} = \tfrac{1}{2}\varepsilon_0 c E_0{}^2 \quad \text{watts per square meter.} \tag{30}$$

The reader may verify that this value corresponds to transport at velocity $c$ of the energy stored in the field, Eq. (4).

To supply this energy flux, power must be expended by external means to maintain a time-varying electric current density **J** in the source.

Taking the divergence of **S**, we find

$$\nabla \cdot \mathbf{S} = \nabla \cdot \mathbf{E} \times \mathbf{H} = \mathbf{E} \cdot \nabla \times \mathbf{H} = \mathbf{E} \cdot \dot{\mathbf{D}} + \mathbf{E} \cdot \mathbf{J}, \tag{31}$$

which vanishes on the average except where components of **J** exist which are properly phased and directed with respect to **E**. Thus, if at the plane $\mathbf{k} \cdot \mathbf{r} = 0$, **J** is parallel to and in phase with the plane wave of Eq. (16),

$$\mathbf{J} = \sigma \mathbf{E}_0 \cos\{\omega_0 t\}, \tag{32}$$

then

$$\mathbf{J} \cdot \mathbf{E} = \sigma E_0{}^2 \cos^2\{\omega_0 t\}, \tag{33}$$

and

$$(\nabla \cdot \mathbf{S})_{\text{avg}} = \tfrac{1}{2}\sigma E_0{}^2 > 0 \quad \text{watts per meter.} \tag{34}$$

This current sheet acts as a source, supplying energy to the wave. Reversal of the phase of $\mathbf{J}$, which inverts the sign of $\mathbf{J} \cdot \mathbf{E}$, produces an absorber, or sink.

The magnitude of the power supplied to the source current uniquely determines the amplitude of the wave field which it creates; the energy flux of the wave arriving at the absorber will determine the amplitude of the induced current, through the coefficient $\sigma$, known as the electrical conductivity.

As a carrier of energy, the electromagnetic wave possesses momentum and imparts reaction forces on its sources and sinks. It can be shown that the momentum flux is the Poynting energy flux divided by the velocity of light.

In terms of the vector potential, the plane wave of Eqs. (16) and (17) may be written as

$$\mathbf{A} = (\mathbf{E}_0/\omega_0) \sin\{\omega_0 t - \mathbf{k}_0 \cdot \mathbf{r}\} = \mathbf{A}_0 \sin\{\omega_0 t - \mathbf{k}_0 \cdot \mathbf{r}\} \tag{35}$$

and the energy flux as

$$S_{\text{avg}} = \tfrac{1}{2}\varepsilon_0 c \omega_0{}^2 A_0{}^2, \tag{36}$$

and the momentum flux is $\tfrac{1}{2}\varepsilon_0 \omega_0{}^2 A_0{}^2$.

## 2.2. ELECTROMAGNETIC THEORY OF LINEAR, ISO-TROPIC MEDIA

### 2.2.1. Constitutive Relations.
Material substances of interest to conventional optics are conveniently classified as conductors and dielectrics, according to the densities and relative influences of bound and unbound charges in determining the electrical behavior. The majority are electrically isotropic and linear. The term "free charges" used in earlier sections does not apply here. Conduction electrons are *unbound*, not *free*; they may move within the interior, but cannot pass beyond the boundary of a conducting body, which remains electrically neutral except possibly for surface charges held by applied fields.

For linear, isotropic substances, the constitutive relations are

$$\mathbf{B} = \mu\mathbf{H}, \tag{37}$$

$$\mathbf{D} = \varepsilon\mathbf{E}, \tag{38}$$

$$\mathbf{J} = \sigma\mathbf{E}, \tag{39}$$

in which $\mu$, $\varepsilon$, and $\sigma$ are constants of the medium and are independent of the field variables, although they do depend on frequency.

In the optical frequency range, it is almost always true that $\mu = \mu_0$. The internal magnetic moments of the medium do not align with the field, and diamagnetic effects are too small to contribute appreciably to the total magnetic induction.

On the other hand, electrons respond readily to optical frequency fields; either $\varepsilon$ or $\sigma$, and occasionally both, have values distinctively different from the vacuum case. Where unbound charges exist, they provide, as we have already seen, an absorption mechanism. Metallic conductors and plasmas contain unbound charges in great quantity and offer very little resistance to their motion within the conductor (high $\sigma$). Dielectrics, on the other hand, are characterized by a dearth of unbound electrons and very low conductivity. Their optical behavior is characterized by transparency and is dominated by displacement, rather than by conduction, currents.

An applied electric field $\mathbf{E}$ displaces the bound charges of a dielectric medium against restoring forces, thereby creating internal dipole moments which give rise to additional lines of electric induction. The sum of the internal dipole moments induced per unit volume is termed the polarization $\mathbf{P}$. Since the term "polarization" is also used in optics in an entirely different sense, we shall take care to distinguish the *charge* polarization, discussed here, from the *wave* polarization, which identifies the plane containing the electric and propagation vectors of an electromagnetic wave.

The charge displacements induced in a dielectric are of several types. The bound charges on which the applied field acts include not only electrons bound in atoms, molecules, or crystal cells, but also ions, of either sign, and permanent dipoles. The latter are ordinarily oriented at random, giving no net polarization; they experience a torque when an electric field is applied which tends to align them with the field direction and so creates a net polarization. In imperfect dielectrics, there are also charges which are relatively free to migrate in the field until they reach interfaces or become trapped. It is the electronic polarization with which we are principally, but not exclusively, concerned in optics, because of its relatively greater response to extremely rapid variations in the applied field.

The total induction in a dielectric is

$$\mathbf{D} = \mathbf{E} + \mathbf{P} \quad \text{coulombs per square meter,} \qquad (40)$$

and in the common case of *linear, isotropic dielectrics*, the induced charge polarization is directly proportional and parallel to the applied field:

$$\mathbf{P} = \chi\varepsilon_0\mathbf{E} \quad \text{coulombs per square meter;} \tag{41}$$

whence the induction is

$$\mathbf{D} = \varepsilon_0(1 + \chi)\mathbf{E} \quad \text{coulombs per square meter.} \tag{42}$$

The dimensionless ratio $\chi$, termed the dielectric susceptibility, contains the essential optical properties of the dielectric. Alternatively, one states the dielectric constant

$$\varepsilon = \varepsilon_0(1 + \chi) \quad \text{coulombs volt}^{-1}\text{ meter}^{-1}, \tag{43}$$

or the macroscopic polarizability

$$\alpha = \varepsilon_0\chi \quad \text{coulombs volt}^{-1}\text{ meter}^{-1}. \tag{44}$$

In *linear, isotropic media*, these quantities are simple scalar constants, independent of the direction and magnitude of the electric field, but not of its frequency. Their frequency dependences will be examined in a later section.

The displacement currents which are caused to flow in a dielectric by a time-varying field include not only the $\varepsilon_0\dot{\mathbf{E}}$ of the vacuum case, but also currents due to the varying charge polarization $\mathbf{P}$, and these can act as secondary sources of electromagnetic waves.

### 2.2.2. Fields and Waves. The first two Maxwell equations reduce to

$$\nabla \cdot \mathbf{E} = 0, \tag{45}$$

$$\nabla \cdot \mathbf{H} = 0, \tag{46}$$

in any *homogeneous, linear, and isotropic dielectric.*

The propagation equations derived from (7) and (8),

$$\nabla \times (\nabla \times \mathbf{E}) + \mu_0\varepsilon_0\ddot{\mathbf{E}} = -\mu_0\varepsilon_0\chi\ddot{\mathbf{E}} - \mu_0\sigma\dot{\mathbf{E}} \tag{47}$$

and

$$\nabla \times (\nabla \times \mathbf{H}) + \mu_0\varepsilon_0\ddot{\mathbf{H}} = -\mu_0\varepsilon_0\chi\ddot{\mathbf{H}} - \mu_0\sigma\dot{\mathbf{H}}, \tag{48}$$

include the effects of all moving charges in the medium; these are collected on the right. Since the electrical conductivity $\sigma$ and dielectric susceptibility $\chi$ appear in exactly the same way in each propagation equation, the electric and magnetic wave fields travel together, as in the vacuum case, but with altered velocity, amplitude ratio, and phase relationships.

The plane wave given by (16) and (17) is a solution only of the left sides of (47) and (48). The right sides, expressing the effect of forced motion of charges under the action of the applied field, contribute a particular integral: another wave driven coherently by the induced charge polarization and conduction currents in the medium. Adding it to the vacuum wave produces a resultant total wave with diminished phase velocity and steadily decreasing amplitude.

This decomposition is ordinarily ignored because Eq. (47) can be solved immediately for the total field and, conveniently, by substituting the complex exponential form (Section 2.1.3)

$$\mathbf{E} = \tfrac{1}{2}\mathbf{E}_0 \exp i\{\omega_0 t - \mathbf{k} \cdot \mathbf{r}\} + \text{comp. conj.} \tag{49}$$

into Eq. (47) and determining the wave vector $\mathbf{k}$. The result contains factors which describe the dissipation of the energy of the wave in forced motion of electrons opposed by viscous resistance forces. In *conductors*, the otherwise free motion of the electrons is interrupted by collisions, which randomize the collective motion, converting its energy to heat; this is embodied in the conductivity $\sigma$. In *dielectrics*, the electrons are bound but execute forced oscillation, and this may also be damped by dissipative processes within the molecule or unit cell, so that the charge polarization lags behind the driving field in phase. Therefore $\chi$ is complex

$$\chi = \chi' - i\chi'' \tag{50}$$

and the wave vector $\mathbf{k}$ is a complex function, the square of which is

$$k^2 = \{1 + \chi' - i[\chi'' + (\sigma/\varepsilon_0\omega_0)]\}\omega_0^2/c^2. \tag{51}$$

The great variety in the optical behavior of linear media is contained in the relative magnitudes of the various constitutive coefficients and in their behavior as functions of the frequency.

In *transparent dielectrics*, the imaginary parts can be neglected; $k$ differs from its vacuum value by the real factor

$$\nu = k/k_0 \doteq (1 + \chi)^{1/2}, \tag{52}$$

called the index of refraction. The phase velocity of the wave is reduced by this factor. The relationship of electric and magnetic fields analogous to Eqs. (22) and (23) is found from the field equations

$$\mathbf{k} \times \mathbf{E}_0 = \omega_0\mu_0\mathbf{H}_0, \tag{53}$$

$$\mathbf{k} \times \mathbf{H}_0 = -\omega_0\varepsilon_0\nu^2\mathbf{E}_0. \tag{54}$$

Thus the wave is transverse, as before, but the ratio of amplitudes of **E** and **H** is changed,

$$|\mathbf{H}_0| = \nu(\varepsilon_0/\mu_0)^{1/2}|\mathbf{E}_0|, \tag{55}$$

the wavelength is shortened,

$$\lambda = 2\pi/k = \lambda_0/\nu, \tag{56}$$

and the energy flux remains parallel to the vector **k** but contains the factor $\nu$, [compare with Eq. (30)],

$$S = \tfrac{1}{2}\nu c\varepsilon_0 E_0^2. \tag{57}$$

With absorption, on the other hand, the imaginary term is not negligible, and the wave is attenuated. If the absorption is weak, we can still use the above relations as a fair approximation.

In *conductors*, the imaginary term cannot be ignored. The field equations for our plane wave become (neglecting dielectric losses)

$$\mathbf{k} \times \mathbf{E}_0 = \omega_0\mu_0\mathbf{H}_0 \tag{58}$$

$$\mathbf{k} \times \mathbf{H}_0 = -\omega_0\varepsilon\mathbf{E}_0 - i\sigma\mathbf{E}_0 \tag{59}$$

and Eq. (51) becomes

$$k^2 = k_0^2[(\varepsilon/\varepsilon_0) + (i\sigma/\varepsilon_0\omega_0)], \tag{60}$$

which is usually written in the form

$$k/k_0 = \nu - i\varkappa \tag{61}$$

where the imaginary part has the magnitude

$$\varkappa = \sigma/2\nu\varepsilon_0\omega_0, \tag{62}$$

called the extinction coefficient, and now

$$\nu = [(\varepsilon/\varepsilon_0) + \varkappa^2]^{1/2} \tag{63}$$

is the index of refraction.

The imaginary term in $k$ now introduces an attenuation factor $\exp\{-\varkappa\mathbf{k}_0 \cdot \mathbf{r}\}$ on the electromagnetic wave, so that the field amplitude diminishes as the wave progresses into the conductor. This is the basis of a well-known phenomenon: the skin effect. Noting that $\omega_0\lambda_0 = 2\pi c$, we find the mean penetration depth to be

$$\lambda_0/2\pi v\varkappa = \sigma/2vc\varepsilon_0 = 188\sigma/v \quad \text{meters.} \tag{64}$$

In conductors, the $\mathbf{E}$ and $\mathbf{H}$ wave fields are no longer in phase, since the relationship between their amplitudes is complex.

It is interesting to consider a medium for which either the conductivity $\sigma$ or the imaginary part of the susceptibility $\chi''$ is negative (at least for a restricted range of frequency). The reader may have encountered the concept of negative resistance elsewhere, most likely in electronics. Ordinary resistance *dissipates* energy; negative resistance entails an energy *supply*. A medium with negative $\sigma$ must have been previously prepared, or "pumped," so as to constitute a reservoir of energy which can be tapped by applying an electric field at the proper frequency. An electromagnetic wave at this frequency will be augmented, rather than attenuated, in a properly pumped medium, since the sign of the extinction coefficient $\varkappa$ is then reversed. This is an instructive way to visualize the stimulated emission of a laser amplifier.

### 2.2.3. Boundary Phenomena.

**2.2.3. Boundary Phenomena.** Much of the subject matter of optics concerns the changes which occur in electromagnetic waves at interfaces between distinct media, in which the transition layer is thin in comparison with the wavelength.

Boundary conditions which apply at an interface require that the components of $\mathbf{D}$ and $\mathbf{B}$ normal to the bounding surface and the components of $\mathbf{E}$ and $\mathbf{H}$ parallel to the surface are continuous at the boundary. To meet these boundary conditions, the directions as well as the magnitudes of the wave vectors differ in the two media, and a symmetrical reflected wave exists in the first medium. The source of the reflected wave is the unequal charge polarization on the two sides of the boundary. Here we shall go into some detail.

Consider a plane, polarized, monochromatic wave, denoted by the subscript $i$, incident on a plane interface separating two dielectric media, the medium on the incident side being fully transparent. Let $r$ denote the reflected and $t$ the transmitted waves. Denote the refractive index on the incident side by $v$, that on the far side by $v'$. Relate these to a rectangular coordinate system with its $XY$ plane coincident with the interface (Figure 3).

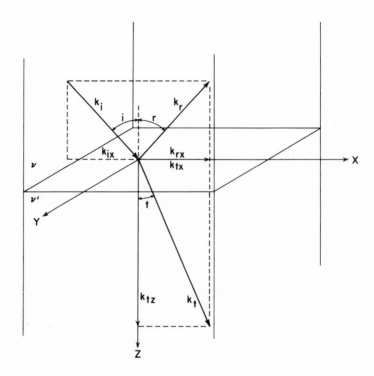

Figure 3. Propagation vectors of incident, refracted, and
reflected light waves at a plane boundary between two optical
media.

The wave vectors are, respectively, $k_i$ for the incident wave, $k_r$ for the
reflected wave, and $k_t$ for the transmitted wave. We have

$$k_i = k_r = \nu k_0, \tag{65}$$

$$k_t = \nu' k_0. \tag{66}$$

The continuity requirements imply that the phase factors of the resultant total fields have equal values on each side of the (optically thin) boundary. This is true only if the components of each **k**-vector parallel to the surface are the same for each wave. The **k**-vectors therefore lie in a common
plane; suppose it to be the $XZ$ plane. Then the $x$ components of all **k**'s
are equal

$$k_{ix} = k_{rx} = k_{tx} \tag{67}$$

or

$$k_i \sin i = k_r \sin r = k_t \sin t, \tag{68}$$

whence

$$v \sin i = v \sin r = v' \sin t, \qquad (69)$$

which is Snell's law of refraction. If $v'$ is complex, the transmitted wave attenuates beyond the boundary.

To relate the respective field amplitudes, we first distinguish the two modes of wave polarization by resolving the electric vector of each wave into components, one with $\mathbf{E}$ directed in the plane of incidence and the other directed normal to that plane. Additional subscripts, $p$ and $s$, refer to these respective cases.

In the $s$ case, each wave contributes to an $\mathbf{E}$ field in the $Y$ direction, and the total electric fields are equal on the two sides of the interface:

$$E_{is} + E_{rs} = E_{ts}. \qquad (70)$$

For the components of $\mathbf{H}$ parallel to the surface, we have, from Eq. (53),

$$\mu_0 \omega_0 H_{ix} = k_{iz} E_{iy} = k_i E_i \cos i = v k_0 E_i \cos i, \qquad (71)$$

$$\mu_0 \omega_0 H_{rx} = k_{rz} E_{ry} = k_i E_i \cos r, \qquad (72)$$

$$\mu_0 \omega_0 H_{tx} = k_{tz} E_{ty} = k_t E_t \cos t. \qquad (73)$$

Continuity requires that

$$H_{ix} + H_{rx} = H_{tx}. \qquad (74)$$

Combining, we obtain Fresnel's formulas relating the amplitudes for $s$-polarized waves

$$\frac{E_r}{E_i} = \frac{k_{iz} - k_{tz}}{k_{iz} + k_{tz}} = \frac{v \cos i - (v'^2 - v^2 \sin^2 i)^{1/2}}{v \cos i + (v'^2 - v^2 \sin^2 i)^{1/2}}, \qquad (75)$$

$$\frac{E_t}{E_i} = \frac{2k_{iz}}{k_{iz} + k_{tz}} = \frac{2v \cos i}{v \cos i + (v'^2 - v^2 \sin^2 i)^{1/2}}. \qquad (76)$$

These predict that $\mathbf{E}_r$ can be oppositely directed to $\mathbf{E}_i$ under appropriate circumstances (e.g., normal incidence, $v > v'$). This is equivalent to a change of phase by 180°.

The corresponding derivation for $p$ polarization is straightforward, except that $\mathbf{H}$ will then lie along the $Y$ direction, so it is simpler to use Eq. (54) and work with the magnetic fields:

$$\frac{H_r}{H_i} = \frac{v'^2 k_{iz} - v^2 k_{tz}}{v'^2 k_{iz} + v^2 k_{tz}}, \qquad (77)$$

$$\frac{H_t}{H_i} = \frac{2\nu'^2 k_{iz}}{\nu'^2 k_{iz} + \nu^2 k_{tz}}. \tag{78}$$

Note that with $p$ polarization, but not with $s$ polarization, the reflected wave can vanish if

$$(\nu'/\nu)^2 = k_{tz}/k_{iz}. \tag{79}$$

By use of Eqs. (68) and (69), one can verify that the reflected and refracted wave vectors are then mutually perpendicular. The particular angle of incidence at which no $p$-polarized light can be reflected, called the Brewster angle, is given by

$$i_B = \arctan (\nu'/\nu). \tag{80}$$

As the angle of incidence $i$ increases, the amplitudes of the reflected wave decrease to zero at the Brewster angle and increase with reversed sign (change of phase) at still larger incident angles.

Another important case is normal incidence. Here the direction of wave polarization does not matter and all the **k** vectors are collinear. The respective Poynting vectors are related as follows:

$$\frac{\mathbf{E}_r \times \mathbf{H}_r}{\mathbf{E}_i \times \mathbf{H}_i} = \frac{(k_i - k_t)}{(k_i + k_t)} \cdot \frac{(\nu'^2 k_i - \nu^2 k_t)}{(\nu'^2 k_i + \nu^2 k_t)} = - \left| \frac{\nu' - \nu}{\nu' + \nu} \right|^2 = R \tag{81}$$

and

$$\frac{\mathbf{E}_t \times \mathbf{H}_t}{\mathbf{E}_i \times \mathbf{H}_i} = \frac{2k_i}{(k_i + k_t)} \cdot \frac{2\nu'^2 k_i}{(\nu'^2 k_i + \nu^2 k_t)} = \frac{2\nu'\nu}{(\nu' + \nu)^2} = T. \tag{82}$$

If the second medium is metallic, we must replace $\nu'$ by $\nu' - i\varkappa'$. If it is highly conductive, the extinction coefficient $\varkappa$ will be the dominant term in the reflection formulas, making the reflection nearly total with reversal of phase. The total electric field therefore vanishes at the surface of a perfect conductor. In practical cases, a highly damped wave penetrates for a short distance into the conductor and the reflected light undergoes changes of phase which differ for the two components of wave polarization.

If both media are transparent but the second is of lower refractive index, $k_t < k_i$, it becomes impossible to meet the requirement of Eq. (67) that the $x$ components of $\mathbf{k}_t$ and $\mathbf{k}_i$ be equal. A transmitted wave does not exist in this, the case of total internal reflection.

## 2.3. MODES

The infinitely extended, monochromatic plane wave of Eqs. (16) and (49) is mathematically simple, and convenient for discussing the elementary phenomena of electromagnetism, but is quite unrealistic. In practice, we deal with finite, transient sources from which fields propagate outward in three-dimensional space, and the propagation equation must be written and, where possible, solved in whatever system of coordinates is appropriate to the special geometrical conditions of the problem. The wave amplitudes will in general be functions of position and time, often giving the wave a rather complicated structure.

Symmetry sometimes makes it possible to express these dependences in terms of characteristic functions of the sphere or cylinder, at least to good approximation.

Any particular solution of the wave propagation equation with a distinct frequency and spatial dependence consistent with the boundary conditions is termed a "wave mode."

A purely monochromatic wave is also only a useful mathematical device. The frequency composition of an electromagnetic wave is determined by the time-dependence of the source.

Since even a pure simple-harmonic alternating current must, in practice, either have begun abruptly or have developed gradually to its existing amplitude and frequency, its Fourier analysis contains more than a single frequency. All of the frequencies of the source current density will be reproduced in the spectrum of the emitted radiation.

The linearity of Eqs. (13), (14), (47), and (48) permits one to construct composite wave fields in which the total field is expressed as a superposition of independently propagating modes which accurately represent observable waves, and in which the descriptions of spatial pattern and time dependence are separable problems.

In a linear dielectric, Eq. (38) applies. Taking its divergence, we find

$$\nabla \cdot \mathbf{E} = \nabla \cdot \mathbf{D} - \mathbf{E} \cdot \nabla \varepsilon \tag{83}$$

and, if it is homogeneous as well, Eq. (45) applies, since then

$$\nabla \varepsilon = 0. \tag{84}$$

The wave propagation equation reduces to

$$\nabla^2 \mathbf{E} - (\nu^2 \dot{\mathbf{E}}/c^2) = 0. \tag{85}$$

Solution of this equation proceeds by first separating the time dependence of $\mathbf{E}$. Representing $\mathbf{E}$ by a Fourier series

$$\mathbf{E} = \Sigma \, \mathbf{E}_\omega(\mathbf{r}) \exp\{i\omega t\} \tag{86}$$

and substituting it in (85), one obtains

$$\nabla^2 \mathbf{E}_\omega + (\nu^2 \omega^2 \mathbf{E}_\omega / c^2) = 0 \tag{87}$$

for the spatial pattern of a wave mode at the frequency $\omega$. The boundary conditions of the particular problem must be known before one can proceed further. It is then a standard boundary value problem, like those encountered in problems of diffusion, heat flow, electrostatics, etc.

A simple example is provided by the Fabry–Perot resonator. Ideally, this comprises a pair of plane, parallel, conducting surfaces spaced a distance $L$ apart, their transverse dimensions large compared with their spacing, and the latter large compared with the wavelength of available radiation.

In this geometry, the wave mode problem reduces to a one-dimensional second-order differential equation, satisfied by trigonometric functions. The steady-state plane wave solution

$$\mathbf{E} = \mathbf{E}_l \sin \{l\pi z / L\}, \tag{88}$$

where $z$ is the distance measured normal to one of the conducting surfaces and $l$ is any integer, satisfies the condition

$$\mathbf{E} = 0, \quad z \le 0, \quad z \ge L,$$

imposed by the vanishing of $\mathbf{E}$ at the conducting boundaries; this restricts the possible frequencies of normally-propagating waves to those for which the argument of the sine function is an integer multiple of $\pi$. Hence the permissible frequencies are

$$\omega = l\pi c / 2\nu L, \tag{89}$$

and any radiation of wavelength

$$\lambda / \nu = 2L / l \tag{90}$$

in the standing wave pattern of Eq. (88) is a permissible mode (Figure 4).

For each allowed frequency, there are two possible independent wave modes, differing in their wave polarization. Thus, there will be $(2\nu L / \pi c)\, d\omega$ discrete normally-directed modes of frequency between $\omega$ and $\omega + d\omega$ in the ideal Fabry–Perot resonator. Note that it is proportional to $L$.

Next, consider the three-dimensional analog of the Fabry–Perot resonator: a cubic enclosure with smooth, perfectly conducting walls. A permissible mode has the form

$$\mathbf{E} = \mathbf{E}_0 \sin \{k_x x\} \sin \{k_y y\} \sin \{k_z z\} \cos \omega t \tag{91}$$

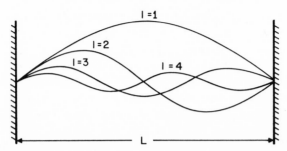

Figure 4. The first four standing-wave modes allowed between two infinite, parallel reflectors. In an optical resonator, of course, the mode index $l$ is a very large number.

provided that

$$k_x = \pi l/L, \qquad k_y = \pi m/L, \qquad k_z = \pi n/L, \tag{92}$$

where $l$, $m$, and $n$ are integers, and that

$$k^2 = k_x{}^2 + k_y{}^2 + k_z{}^2 = (v\omega/c)^2. \tag{93}$$

This has the required property of vanishing on each bounding surface. By extension of the above procedure, one finds that when $L$ is very large, the number of permissible values of $k$ in the range $(k, dk)$ is

$$(1/\pi^2)L^3 k^2 \, dk = (1/\pi^2 c^3)L^3 v^3 \omega^2 \, d\omega, \tag{94}$$

proportional to $L^3$. Hence the density of modes per unit frequency interval is

$$\varrho(\omega) = v^3 \omega^2 / \pi^2 c^3 \tag{95}$$

regardless of the size of $L$.

Without reflecting boundaries, there are an infinite number of modes, of course, but their frequency density is still this definite quantity. The cubic enclosure is a convenient artifice for evaluating it.

To calculate the total field, which is the sum of all the separate modes for each of the allowed frequency components, one must also know the time dependence of the source, or its equivalent, the spectral composition of the light.

An important common case of time dependence is the sinusoidal source current with exponentially decaying amplitude. This situation is encountered when the supply of power to maintain an alternating electric source current is terminated abruptly. Despite the single frequency, the radiation is not monochromatic, because of its varying amplitude.

For an oscillator of frequency $\omega_0$ damped with the factor $\exp\{-\gamma t\}$, Fourier analysis reveals a distribution of frequencies centered at $\omega_0$, their envelope falling to half at

$$|\omega - \omega_0| = \gamma \qquad (96)$$

and diminishing rapidly to zero at frequencies outside this band. This is called a Lorentzian distribution; atomic spectral lines are observed to have this form when conditions are such that Doppler effects due to thermal motion are negligible.

## 2.4. GEOMETRICAL OPTICS

In by far the majority of optical devices and interaction phenomena, one deals with media which are isotropic and homogeneous over regions large compared with the wavelength. Moreover, they are usually either highly transparent (e.g., glass) or strongly absorbing (e.g., metallic reflectors), with boundaries sharply defined and usually symmetrical, such that the wave modes are adequately represented by the simple eigenfunctions of rectangular, spherical, or cylindrical coordinates.

In these problems our concern is with the direction and intensity of energy transport, rather than with the detailed structure of the wave fields. The approximation known as "geometrical optics" is then preferable to a complete description of the field in terms of wave structure, the province of "physical optics." This representation depicts light propagation phenomena in terms of the geometry of rays.

In the steady state in which the time-averaged energy density at each point of an optical field does not change, the divergence of the energy flux vanishes,

$$\nabla \cdot \mathbf{S} = 0, \qquad (97)$$

implying that one can construct continuous lines from sources to absorbers, the directions of which are the directions of energy transport. Their flux through any element of a surface is the intensity of energy flow at that element. These are "light rays;" bundles of rays are called "beams." In optically isotropic media, the direction of a ray is that of the wave vector $\mathbf{k}$, normal to the surfaces of constant phase, called "wavefronts." They are reflected and refracted at discontinuities in the medium as shown in Section 2.2.3.

The fact that at interfaces between dielectrics, light rays are split into reflected and refracted portions gives no difficulty. Their subsequent courses can be examined separately using Snell's law and the transmission-reflection coefficients. When two beams formed by division of a wave are subsequently made to overlap, one may expect observable interference phenomena in the resultant field structure, but no modification in the ray geometry of either beam (if the overlap region contains an optically linear medium). This is because of the property of superposition of solutions of the linear wave equation.

There are important limitations to the validity of geometrical optics. The ray concept is valid only when the wavefront extends appreciably in every direction normal to the ray. The induction at each point in a wave-front contributes to establishing the field at all points reached later by the wave. Whenever a light beam is limited in its extent by apertures, waves spread, carrying energy into the region outside the beam predicted by geometrical optics.

The approximate nature of geometrical optics is illustrated by the problem of focusing a light beam with a properly shaped reflecting or refracting surface. According to geometrical optics, one thereby creates a conical beam of converging rays which intersect at a focal point. It does not follow that the intensity at the focal point is infinite, however. According to physical optics one cannot establish a wave field of arbitrarily small dimensions. The intensity can vanish only at those points outside the focal region for which wavelets arising from different elements of the lens aperture arrive so phased as to give complete cancellation. For an adequate description of this phenomenon, one must calculate the mode pattern established by the lens at its focal plane, spherical Bessel functions being appropriate to this geometry.

The intensity at the focus is not infinite, as analysis shows the energy is spread over a region at least $1.22f\lambda$ in diameter, where $f$ is the focal/aperture ratio of the lens; the intensity is said to be "diffraction-limited." This diffraction disk for ruby-laser light at $f/4$ is $3.4\,\mu$ in diameter.

# 2.5. QUANTUM THEORY OF RADIATION PROCESSES

**2.5.1. Photons.** The electromagnetic theory of light represents the wave fields $\mathbf{E}$ and $\mathbf{H}$ and the vector potential $\mathbf{A}$ as continuous functions of space and time. Their interactions with electric charges in matter are also represented as continuous. The coefficients of the constitutive relations

Eqs. (37–39) are constants, and the polarization, magnetization, and current density are, like the fields which induce them, continuous functions.

We know, however, that this also is only an approximation, valid when fields are not too weak and the numbers of atoms, molecules, or unit electronic systems are large enough to be statistically well-defined. Optical media consist of atoms, distributed either at random or grouped as molecules or crystal cells. The dipole moment of an individual atom, molecule, or unit cell has only certain discrete values. The apparently continuous range of values of **P** is accounted for in terms of large numbers of atoms associated with each allowed value, and its apparently continuous variation with **E** must consist in a great many individual transitions of atoms from one electronic state to another per unit time. Each transition involves a quantized exchange of energy between the electronic system and the radiation field, the probability for which is related to the field variable. The field, having been built up by discrete additions, must also consist of quanta, or photons. Their flux density $\phi$ determines the applicable values of the field variables. Interactions involve their emission, absorption, or scattering.

Since light possesses momentum, we must attribute to each photon its share of the momentum of the light beam. This is clearly its energy $\hbar\omega$ divided by the velocity of light $c/v$; i.e., the propagation vector multiplied by $\hbar$. This relation is verified experimentally; in particular, by the Compton effect.

How good is the continuous-field approximation. The energy flux $S$ is (Eq. 57)

$$S = \tfrac{1}{2}\varepsilon_0 E_0^2 vc = 1.327(-3)vE_0^2 \quad \text{watts per square meter,}$$

and the corresponding flux of photons, each of energy $\hbar\omega$, is

$$\phi = S/\hbar\omega = 5.04(24)S\lambda_0 \quad \text{photons per square meter per second.} \quad (98)$$

The enormous coefficient 5.04(24) justifies continuous-field theory for nearly all practical ranges of $S$. For example, consider a He–Ne laser producing 1(3) W/m² at a wavelength 0.635(−6) m. The corresponding values are:

$$\omega = 2.97(15) \text{ sec}^{-1}$$

$$\hbar\omega = 1.96 \text{ eV} = 3.13(-19) \text{ J}$$

$$\phi = 3.20(21) \text{ photons m}^{-2} \text{ sec}^{-1}$$

$$E_0 = 870 \text{ V m}^{-1} \textit{ in vacuo, } v = 1$$

$$A_0 = E_0/\omega = 293(-15) = 293(-13) \text{ V sec m}^{-1}$$

The constitutive coefficients of Eqs. (37)–(39) may be regarded as measures of the cross section for the interaction of photons with the electron systems of the medium.

A beam of particles passing through a region containing atoms with which collisions may occur is attenuated exponentially; a light wave is also attenuated exponentially when the extinction coefficient $\varkappa$ is appreciable.

Let $q_a$ denote the cross section for an absorbing collision, and, noting that the *intensity* attenuation of a wave is the square of that for either field variable, formally equate the respective attenuation factors:

$$\exp(-2\varkappa k_0 \cdot r) = \exp(-Nq_a^2). \tag{99}$$

One finds that

$$q_a = \varkappa k_0/Nf_c \qquad \text{meters}^{-1}/\text{meters}^{-3}$$
$$= \omega_0/2\nu c\varepsilon_0 Nf_c \quad \text{meters}^2 \tag{100}$$

relates the electrical conductivity to the cross section for direct photon absorption by the $f_c$ conduction electrons associated with each of the $N$ atoms per unit volume. Similarly, one relates the real part of the dielectric susceptibility to a cross section for their absorption by bound charges of each atom, provided one can determine the effective number of electrons per atom.

## 2.5.2. Calculation of Interaction Coefficients. Calculation of these interaction coefficients requires quantum-mechanical analysis of two interacting subsystems, one comprising the radiation field and the other the optically effective electrons, which move in a potential field appropriate to the atom, molecule, or solid which contains them. To this purpose it is first necessary to express the total energy of the electronic system as a function of the coordinates and momenta, i.e., to write its Hamiltonian function.

One then rewrites the latter as a Schrödinger equation

$$\mathscr{H}\psi = E\psi \tag{101}$$

by replacing the momenta with operators

$$\mathbf{p} \to i\hbar\boldsymbol{\nabla}, \text{ etc.}, \tag{102}$$

and the energy with the operator

$$E \to -i\hbar(\partial/\partial t). \tag{103}$$

Letting these operate on the wave function $\psi$ and solving the resulting differential equation with appropriate boundary conditions gives the allowed wave functions $u_n \exp\{-i\omega_n t\}$ and stationary-state energies $\hbar\omega_n$ of the electronic system. These constitute a complete set of orthonormal functions, out of which the initial conditions may select a particular combination appropriate to a specified problem. The problem is mathematically similar to that of determining the modes and characteristic frequencies of the classical radiation field.

An isolated electronic system may be in any one of the stationary states characterized by a particular set of quantum numbers; usually, we know only enough to assign probabilities for the occupancy of given states, writing the wave function as a series with constant coefficients

$$\psi_n = \sum_n a_n u_n \exp\{-i\omega_n t\}. \tag{104}$$

We interpret the quantity

$$\psi_n \bar{\psi}_n = |\, a_n \,|^2$$

as the probability that the electronic system occupies the state identified by the quantum number $n$, provided that the wave function is normalized so that

$$\sum_n \psi_n \bar{\psi}_n \, dV = 1. \tag{105}$$

The quantity

$$\langle e\mathbf{r} \rangle \equiv \int \bar{\psi}_n (e\mathbf{r}) \psi_n \, dV \tag{106}$$

is the average or expectation value of the dipole moment of the electronic subsystem in the $n$th stationary state.

The other subsystem is regarded as an assemblage of harmonic oscillators, each corresponding to an allowed mode of the radiation field. The eigenvalues of a harmonic oscillator in quantum mechanics are $(N + \frac{1}{2})\hbar\omega$; i.e., it contains an integral number $N$ of quanta of excitation (photons) each of energy $\hbar\omega$ above a "zero-point" energy $\hbar\omega/2$. Changes of the quantum number $N$ require the emission or absorption of light quanta by charged particles, i.e., an interaction between these two subsystems.

The interaction of the electronic system with radiation is treated as a perturbation which affects the coefficients but not the forms of these solutions. Nonrelativistic electrons interact principally with the electric component, which does work at a rate $e(\mathbf{v} \cdot \mathbf{E})$ watts. An interaction term $e(\mathbf{v} \cdot \mathbf{A})$

is added to the Hamiltonian which corresponds to this perturbation, using the vector potential defined in Section 2.1.2.

A complete treatment adds an additional term to the interaction. The complete interaction is

$$\mathscr{H}_1 = e(\mathbf{v} \cdot \mathbf{A}) + (e^2/2m)A^2. \tag{107}$$

The interaction, being weak, disturbs but does not appreciably change the character of either system; its allowed states and wave functions are the same as before, but they are no longer stationary. Transitions are induced from one state to another, so that their probabilities of occupancy $|a_n|^2$ are functions of the time during the period of interaction.

Quantum-mechanical analysis of the interaction proceeds by finding a solution of the complete Schrödinger equation

$$(\mathscr{H} + \mathscr{H}_1)\psi = i\hbar\dot{\psi} \tag{108}$$

in the form of a series

$$\psi = \sum_l b_l(t)u_l \exp\{-i\omega_l t\} \tag{109}$$

which is like that of the unperturbed system except that the coefficients $b_l$ are functions of time.

Substitution of this series produces a set of coupled first-order differential equations for the variable probability amplitudes $b_l$.

This array of equations reduces to tractability when it is applied to a particular problem of great practical importance; namely, that in which the total system is known to be initially in a particular state and one inquires the probability that switching on the interaction will induce a transition of the electronic system to another particular state, while, simultaneously, a photon is either emitted or absorbed, as required to conserve the total energy. In doing this one must not forget that the radiation subsystem has a continuous spectrum, with many modes capable of containing the energy of transition between states of the electronic system.

The quantity

$$W(t) = \int |b_n(\omega, t)|^2 \varrho(\omega) \, d\omega \tag{110}$$

expresses the total probability that after a time $t$, the electronic system initially in state $m$ will have made a direct transition to state $n$ by exchanging a photon with one of the available modes of the radiation field.

To evaluate $b_n(t)$, we reduce the infinite set of amplitude equations

$$\sum_k \dot{b}_k \psi_k = -(i/\hbar) \mathcal{H}_1 \sum_l b_l \psi_l \qquad (111)$$

corresponding to (108) and (109) by assuming that the initial condition

$$b_m(0) = 1, \quad b_l(0) = 0 \quad \text{for} \quad l \neq m \qquad (112)$$

is approximately true over the entire time considered, so that

$$\sum_k \dot{b}_k \psi_k = -(i/\hbar) \mathcal{H}_1 \psi_m. \qquad (113)$$

This equation is reduced further when it is multiplied by the complex conjugate of the wave function of the final state $\bar{\psi}_n$ and integrated over the system volume. The wave functions are orthogonal and normalized to represent a single electronic system; hence

$$\int \bar{u}_n u_k \, dV = 1, \quad k = n;$$
$$= 0, \quad k \neq n, \qquad (114)$$

and (113) reduces to the differential equation for the $n$th state coefficient alone:

$$\dot{b}_n = -(i/\hbar) \int \bar{\psi}_n \mathcal{H}_1 \psi_m \, dV$$
$$= -(i/\hbar) | \mathcal{H}_{mn} | \exp\{i\omega_{mn} t\}, \qquad (115)$$

where $\omega_{mn}$ is the frequency of radiation with photon energy equal to the energy difference between the two stationary states, and

$$\mathcal{H}_{mn} = \int \bar{u}_n \mathcal{H}_1 u_m \, dV \qquad (116)$$

represents the interaction energy $\mathcal{H}$ averaged over the initial and final states of the electronic system. The various quantities $\mathcal{H}_{mn}$ characterize the effect of the interaction with respect to various pairs of states; they constitute a matrix, and are called "matrix elements."

Finally, Eq. (115) is solved for $[b_n(t)]^2$ and summed over the available radiation modes, giving the direct transition probability. It is found to be proportional to the time of interaction.

This procedure accounts for some but not all of the radiative transitions which are observed to occur between states of an electronic system. In many cases, the direct matrix element vanishes, and the approximation must be extended by including the possibility of indirect transitions from state $m$ to state $n$ by means of one or more intermediate states, $n', n'', \ldots,$

etc. The general result for the transition probability per unit time is

$$W_{mn} = 2\pi \, | \, \mathcal{H}_1(\omega_{mn}) \, |^2 \varrho(\omega_{mn})/\hbar^2, \tag{117}$$

where

$$\mathcal{H}_1(\omega_{mn}) = \mathcal{H}_{mn} \tag{118}$$

for direct transitions, $m \rightarrow n$;

$$\mathcal{H}_1(\omega_{mn}) = \sum_{n'} \frac{\mathcal{H}_{mn'} \mathcal{H}_{n'n}}{E_m - E_{n'}} \tag{119}$$

for a single intermediate state, $m \rightarrow n' \rightarrow n$;

$$\mathcal{H}_1(\omega_{mn}) = \sum_{n',n''} \frac{\mathcal{H}_{mn'} \mathcal{H}_{n'n''} \mathcal{H}_{n''n}}{(E_m - E_{n'})(E_{n'} - E_{n''})} \tag{120}$$

for two intermediate states, etc. The density of radiation modes was found in Section 2.3.

The matrix elements of the interaction of an electronic system with radiation are determined not only by relevant features of the structure of the electronic system, but also by the mode structure and intensity of the radiation field, which is contained in the vector potential $\mathbf{A}$ in Eq. (107). In general, as many as four quantum numbers are required to characterize the electronic structure of the source or absorber system, and the same number of indices may be required to describe the spatial pattern and polarization of the related wave mode.

We saw in Section 2.1.4 that a classical charge distribution acts either as a source or as an absorber of radiation, depending on whether it is coupled to an energy source or to a load (or to the relative phases of $\mathbf{J}$ and $\mathbf{E}$). The transitions of the electronic system induced by the radiation field interaction may be either absorbing or emitting, depending on its initial state (ground or excited). Note also that the probability of direct transition contains as a factor the square of the Fourier component of the vector potential at the transition frequency; by Eq. (36), this is proportional to the intensity of the radiation and, therefore, to the photon flux density.

Because the radiation field contains unavailable zero-point energy, $A$ is not zero even when *observable* photons (i.e., capable of inducing upward transitions) are not present. The spontaneous emission from an excited system is sometimes explained as the stimulated emission corresponding to this zero-point perturbation energy.

# 3.
# PROPERTIES OF OPTICAL MEDIA

## 3.1. INTRODUCTION

The preceding chapters have described the classical theory of light and outlined the quantum-theoretical basis for explaining its interactions with matter. This chapter describes certain significant properties of optical media known for many years.

The basic mechanism of each effect is explained in classical terms; quantum-mechanical modifications are indicated where they are essential to correct calculation of the interaction coefficients. The description of the propagation of light subject to these interactions is classical, and, wherever possible, in terms of geometrical optics.

This exposition, for which we have previously established a conceptual foundation, provides a natural introduction to the nonlinear phenomena which are currently under investigation. The reader will discover that the latter have really been ready for discovery for many years, awaiting the techniques which could make them observable. They have counterparts in phenomena long known to specialists, but the intense beams and the precision and sensitivity of measurement which are essential to accurate description and prediction have come only recently.

Our concern in the remainder of this monograph is with the propagation of light in various material media which may be interposed between sources and absorbers, rather than with its emission and absorption. Nevertheless, it will be necessary to refer often to the characteristic frequencies of optical media, which are most directly revealed in emission and absorption spectroscopy. For this reason, we must mention the Zeeman and Stark effects, which are ordinarily categorized as emission phenomena.

## 3.2. DISPERSION

That the majority of optically interesting media are dielectrics is of course due to their relatively high transparency; their most important optical characteristic is the frequency dependence of the index of refraction, termed dispersion. Normally, the index of refraction increases with increasing frequency of the light. However, strong absorption occurs at certain characteristic frequencies, and the index of refraction undergoes an apparently discontinuous drop as the frequency is raised through the absorption line. Figure 5 illustrates this phenomenon, which is called "anomalous dispersion."

It was shown in Section 2.2 that the index of refraction of a dielectric is proportional to the square root of the ratio of the dielectric constant $\varepsilon$ to the vacuum value $\varepsilon_0$. In linear dielectrics, $\varepsilon$ is independent of the electric

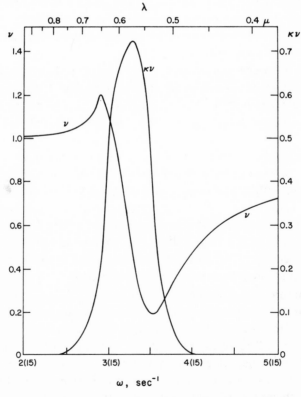

Figure 5. The index of refraction $\nu$ and absorption index $\nu\varkappa$ of cyanin, showing anomalous dispersion near an absorption resonance.

field intensity $\mathbf{E}$; this was shown to imply direct proportionality of the induced polarization $\mathbf{P}$ to the electric field intensity $\mathbf{E}$.

The classical microscopic theory of dispersion interprets this proportionality as indicative of Hooke's law binding forces on the atomic electrons, which are forced to oscillate by the electric field of the incoming wave. The magnetic field component is weak and does not appreciably affect the electron's path or environment. The macroscopic polarization is the electric dipole moment induced per unit volume,

$$\mathbf{P} = Ne \sum_j f_j \mathbf{x}_j = \varepsilon_0 \chi \mathbf{E}, \qquad (121)$$

from the displacements $\mathbf{x}_j$ of $f_j$ electrons of type $j$ within each atomic unit, $N$ being the concentration of atomic unit cells. These displacements obey the forced harmonic oscillator equation

$$\ddot{\mathbf{x}} + g_j \dot{\mathbf{x}} + \omega_j^2 \mathbf{x} = \mathbf{E}e/m. \qquad (122)$$

Let $\mathbf{E}_0 \exp\{i\omega_0 t\}$ denote an impressed wave of frequency $\omega_0$, and solve for $\mathbf{x}_j$; the electric susceptibility is found to be

$$\chi = \frac{Ne^2}{m\varepsilon_0} \sum_j \frac{f_j}{\omega_j^2 - \omega_0^2 - ig_j\omega_0} = \chi' - i\chi'' \qquad (123)$$

a complex number, of which

$$\chi' = \frac{Ne^2}{m\varepsilon_0} \sum_j \frac{f_j(\omega_j^2 - \omega_0^2)}{(\omega_j^2 - \omega_0^2)^2 + g_j^2\omega_0^2} \qquad (124)$$

is the real part, and

$$\chi'' = -\frac{Ne^2}{m\varepsilon_0} \sum_j \frac{f_j g_j \omega_0}{(\omega_j^2 - \omega_0^2)^2 + g_j^2\omega_0^2} \qquad (125)$$

is the imaginary part.*

---

* In the complete theory, one introduces a correction which takes account of the slight difference between the effective electric field intensity (which acts on an individual electronic system to polarize it), and the total field (which includes that system's contribution). The susceptibility then is found to be not strictly proportional to the density of the dielectric, as is implied by the factor $N$ in Eqs. (121)–(125). Instead, it is found that the quantity $\chi/(3 + \chi)$, rather than $\chi$ itself, is proportional to the atomic concentration. This more precise relation is known as the Clausius–Mosotti law. The constant of proportionality involves the detailed geometry of each particular kind of molecule or crystal cell structure. In gases, the correction is unimportant because $\chi$ is small in comparison with unity.

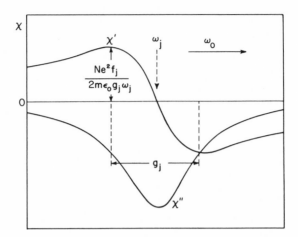

Figure 6. The real and imaginary components of the dielectric susceptibility for frequencies in the vicinity of a single natural frequency.

The two components of the complex susceptibility are plotted against the frequency in Figure 6. The width of each absorption line is determined by the damping constant $g_j$; its position by the natural frequency $\omega_j$; and the magnitude of its contribution to the susceptibility by the oscillator strength $f_j$. This should be compared with the expression obtained in Section 2.3 for the shape of an emission line (also compare Figures 5 and 6).

The constants for each line must be determined empirically to fit the observed refractive index to the dispersion formula.

Quantum mechanics goes much further, enabling the constants of the dispersion formula to be calculated. The natural frequencies correspond to transitions between stationary states of the atomic system, the $f_j$ measure the matrix elements of the respective transitions, and the damping constants $g_j$ are determined by the total energy uncertainty of the combining stationary states.

Figure 7 shows the coherent scattering process from the quantum-mechanical standpoint. The atom ordinarily occupies its ground state before and after the event. In the presence of photons of energy $\hbar\omega$, it makes a temporary transition to an intermediate state, $i$ or $i'$; in the former case, it first absorbs and then reemits; in the latter case, emission precedes absorption. The intermediate state may be regarded as a superposition of the various stationary states of the atom (energy conservation does not restrict the intermediate state, because of its transitory existence.) The transition probability is calculated by perturbation theory, as described in Section

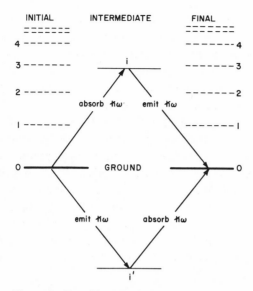

Figure 7. Transitions to intermediate states in
the quantum-mechanical model of dispersion.

2.5.2. Using the first-order interaction term $e(\mathbf{v} \cdot \mathbf{A})$, matrix elements are obtained connecting the initial (final) state with each of the stationary states; each is divided by the difference between the energy of the respective state and the intermediate state. The result is summed and integrated over the spectrum of the radiation field.

The resulting dispersion formula is identical in its dependence on photon energy (frequency) with the classical formula. However, matrix elements, which are (in principle, at least) calculable from the internal structure of the atomic system, replace the empirically determined oscillator strengths. The finite widths of the combining states determine the width of each absorption line corresponding to the damping factor $g_j$ of the classical model.

Most important, the quantum-mechanical model applies to inelastic processes, in which the final state differs from the initial state, and it accounts for negative dispersion, in which any initial population of an excited state reduces, rather than adds, to the susceptibility, because of stimulated emission.

In both classical and quantum models, linearity is only a first approximation. The classical atomic-dipole oscillator is linear if the potential well within which the dispersion electron moves is strictly quadratic in the displacement. In the quantum model, with the $e(\mathbf{v} \cdot \mathbf{A})$ interaction, only one photon interacts at a time with the atomic system; the energies and populations of the various stationary states of the atom are not appreciably perturbed by the electromagnetic field. This is true if the light wave is of limited intensity. At higher intensity, the $A^2$ term in the interaction Hamiltonian becomes significant, and the atoms may attain an appreciable excited-state population by ground-state absorption.

The field intensities in light waves are ordinarily of such low amplitude that nonlinearities are unobservable. However, static fields can readily be applied to optical media in sufficient strength to perturb their refractive properties, giving rise to a variety of "effects," which will be described below. An extreme example is the electrical breakdown of a dielectric by strong dc electric field; this demonstrates strikingly that the binding of polarization charges cannot be linear at high field intensities; their potential well is not of infinite height, and deviations from linearity must be expected as they approach the surface of the well when displaced far from their normal positions.

## 3.3. RAYLEIGH SCATTERING

In Section 2.2.2, we showed that the combination of a coherently scattered wave with the vacuum wave gives rise to the index of refraction; the amplitude of the coherently scattered wave relates to the real part of the macroscopic susceptibility $\chi$ found by multiplying the density $N$ of atomic systems per unit volume by the atomic susceptibility, which, as we have just seen, describes the forced oscillation of dispersion electrons.

The validity of multiplying by $N$ implies that the number of molecules $N \Delta V$ in a microscopic volume element $\Delta V$ of dimensions comparable with one half-wavelength is so large that its statistical fluctuation from element to element is negligible. The intensity of radiation scattered by dipoles induced in each element is then so nearly uniform throughout the medium that, except in the forward direction, where the path differences and phase differences compensate (Figure 8), cancellation by interference takes place among the wavelets scattered by the various elements. This cancellation is not quite complete, however.

Imagine a gaseous medium subdivided into volume elements in the form of small cubes $\lambda/2$ on a side (Figure 8). The radiation scattered by two adjacent elements will be in phase in the forward direction but oppositely phased at 90°; if they contain exactly equal numbers of molecules, there will be no 90° scattering. However, for green light, $\lambda = 5(-7)$ m, the volume of each element will be $\lambda^3 = 1.6(-20)$ m³, and, at atmospheric pressure,

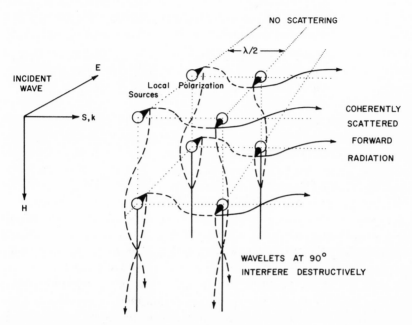

Figure 8. Coherent scattering of light by elementary dipoles induced in a medium by an electromagnetic wave incident from the left. Wavelets reradiated by the dipoles interfere, constructively in the forward direction, destructively to the side normal to the plane of polarization.

it will contain approximately

$$N\lambda^3 = [2.7(25) \quad m^{-3}] \times [1.6(-20) \quad m^3]$$
$$= 4(5) \quad \text{molecules}$$

on the average. The root-mean-square fluctuation, approximately 600 molecules, is 0.15% of the total number. At shorter wavelengths, these numbers are less, but the fluctuations become more pronounced. These produce the net scattering.

This phenomenon is responsible for the blue color of the sky. It is called Rayleigh scattering. The scattered power is proportional to the total number of scattering centers and to the fourth power of the frequency. The scattered light is incoherent.

Crystalline media are relatively transparent because the regular arrangement of atoms in the crystal lattice reduces the fluctuations. Thermal motion nevertheless causes slight random fluctuations of density. Light is therefore scattered not only by gases and liquids, but also by crystalline media.

The Rayleigh scattering reduces the intensity of a light beam without actually absorbing the radiation. The term "extinction" is used to denote the attenuation of a beam of light by scattering, as distinct from true absorption.

## 3.4. THE DEBYE-SEARS EFFECT

This effect is manifested by increased scattering of light by a dielectric when sound waves are simultaneously present.

A sound wave passing through a fluid medium may augment its Rayleigh scattering, since the condensations give rise to greater scattering amplitudes than the rarefactions and these variations of density are spatially periodic. In certain directions with respect to the wave vectors of incident light and sound waves, therefore, an ultrasonic (i.e., sufficiently short) wave can act as a weak diffraction grating, and thereby give rise to a coherent component in the scattered light. Since the pattern of condensations and rarefactions moves at sonic velocity, the diffracted light will have a Doppler shift. The changed frequency of course implies an exchange of quanta with the medium.

Figure 9 illustrates the diffraction of light by a plane sound wave.

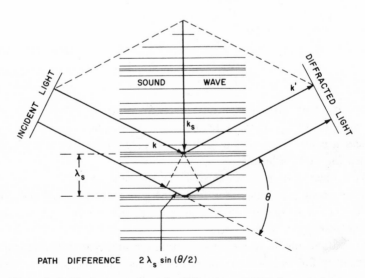

Figure 9. Brillouin scattering—the diffraction of light by sound waves.

Each condensation plane (crest) scatters somewhat more light than the adjacent rarefaction plane (trough). If the path difference between rays diffracted by pairs of adjacent crests or troughs equals an integer multiple of the wavelength of the light, the corresponding scattering will be coherent. This condition was first stated by Brillouin in 1922 as

$$m\lambda = 2\lambda_s \sin\{\theta/2\}, \qquad m = 1, 2, 3, \ldots, \tag{126}$$

but only the situation, not the formula, was new, since the identical relation applies to a diffraction grating and to Bragg scattering of X rays by the atomic planes of a crystal lattice.

In terms of the propagation constants, an equivalent form is

$$mk_s = 2k \sin\{\theta/2\}, \tag{127}$$

and the dispersion relations then lead to

$$m\omega_s/v_s = 2(v\omega/c) \sin\{\theta/2\}, \tag{128}$$

involving the frequencies of the two waves (and their respective velocities).

If each side is multiplied by $\hbar$, the resulting equation can be considered to express a momentum balance, the left side being the momentum of the $m$ sound quanta (phonons) which are emitted to conserve momentum when a photon of momentum $\hbar k$ is deflected by the angle $\theta$. The energy of the phonons is supplied by a reduction in the photon energy corresponding to the Doppler shift.

The Doppler formula for the frequency shift of light scattered by a target moving at velocity $v_s$ is

$$\Delta\omega/\omega = (vv_s/2) \sin\{\theta/2\}. \tag{129}$$

The energy of the phonon is the difference in the photon's energy before and after the scattering event, and is therefore

$$\hbar\,\Delta\omega = (v\omega v_s/2) \sin\{\theta/2\} = m\hbar\omega_s. \tag{130}$$

A more concise representation employs the wave vector $\mathbf{k}$, which when multiplied by $\hbar$ gives the photon momentum. The energy balance is

$$m\omega_s = \omega - \omega', \tag{131}$$

and

$$m\mathbf{k}_s = \mathbf{k} - \mathbf{k}' \tag{132}$$

is the momentum balance, the Planck constant being omitted because it occurs in every term. Figure 9 illustrates this vector relationship.

In solid dielectrics, sound contains transverse as well as longitudinal waves, and there is the possibility of spatially periodic birefringence associated with the sonic disturbances. Thus the complete situation can become extremely complicated in certain crystals.

The scattering of one kind of wave by another is really less remarkable and more common than it seems at first thought. The scattering of waves by any kind of particles can always be reanalyzed, of course, with the latter represented by DeBroglie waves, in terms identical with those used above to explain the Debye–Sears effect. This is the basis of one well-known theory of the Compton effect. Bragg scattering of X rays in crystals is an example. Comprehensive treatments of this general class of physical phenomenon have been given.

## 3.5. BIREFRINGENCE

We saw in Section 2.2.2 that the index of refraction arises from the phase lag between the impressed electric field and radiation from oscillations that field induces in bound charges of the medium. Each oscillating charge was pictured there as bound to an atom or molecule by a Hooke-law type of restoring force; it moves in a field for which the potential energy is proportional to the square of the displacement of the electron from equilibrium in any direction, i.e., a harmonic potential well. In crystals, it is the unit cell of the crystal, rather than an individual atom within the cell, to which the dispersion electrons are bound. The details of the susceptibility tensor are determined by the spatial arrangement and kinds of the various atoms which compose the unit cell and the constraints their arrangement imposes on the dispersion electrons. The potential well in which the dispersion electrons oscillate is isotropic only in the case of cubic lattices.*

It has long been known that many transparent media are optically anisotropic. Double refraction is exhibited by 20 of the 32 crystal classes, and noncrystalline media become doubly refracting when subjected to internal stress, a phenomenon called photoelasticity, which mechanical engineers have found very useful. The constitutive properties $\varepsilon$, $\mu$, and $\sigma$ are functions of the directions of propagation and wave polarization in these media.

Mathematically, these quantities become second-rank tensors in aniso-

---

* Moreover, even then it can not be a *harmonic* well for large displacement amplitudes.

tropic media. Equation (38) becomes a set of three equations of form

$$D_i = \sum_j \varepsilon_{ij}(\omega)E_j, \qquad i = 1, 2, 3, \tag{133}$$

which can also be written

$$D_i \varepsilon_0^{-1} = (\delta_{ij} + \chi_{ij})E_j, \tag{134}$$

using the convention that summation is to be performed over that index which appears more than once on any term (in this case, over $j = 1, 2, 3$), and using the Kronecker $\delta$ symbol, which is unity if $i = j$, zero otherwise.

The single quantity $\varepsilon$ is replaced by an array, or matrix, of nine frequency-dependent components which relate the three components of **D** to the three components of **E**.

Written out in matrix form and in rectangular coordinates, Eq. (134) is

$$\frac{1}{\varepsilon_0} \cdot \begin{pmatrix} D_x \\ D_y \\ D_z \end{pmatrix} = \begin{pmatrix} 1 + \chi_{xx} & \chi_{xy} & \chi_{xz} \\ \chi_{yx} & 1 + \chi_{yy} & \chi_{yz} \\ \chi_{zx} & \chi_{zy} & 1 + \chi_{zz} \end{pmatrix} \cdot \begin{pmatrix} E_x \\ E_y \\ E_z \end{pmatrix}. \tag{135}$$

Thus **D** does not necessarily have the same direction as **E**. This has important consequences. The Maxwell field equations for a plane wave are still [Eqs. (53), (54)]

$$\mathbf{k} \times \mathbf{E} = \omega\mu_0\mathbf{H}, \tag{136}$$

$$\mathbf{k} \times \mathbf{H} = -\omega\mathbf{D}, \tag{137}$$

and the Poynting vector is still [Eq. (30)]

$$\mathbf{S} = \mathbf{E} \times \mathbf{H}. \tag{138}$$

However, in the propagation equation obtained by eliminating **H** in Eqs. (136) and (137),

$$\mu_0\omega^2\mathbf{D} = k^2\mathbf{E} - (\mathbf{k} \cdot \mathbf{E})\mathbf{k}, \tag{139}$$

the term containing $(\mathbf{k} \cdot \mathbf{E})$ does not vanish.

These vectors are shown in Figure 10. In media which are isotropic, **D** is collinear with **E** and **S** with **k**. In media with a tensor relation between induction and field, however, **D** is *not* necessarily parallel to **E**, and it follows that **S** is not necessarily parallel to **k**; i.e., energy propagates in a direction other than that of phase advance. Moreover, the angle $\alpha$ between **S** and **k**,

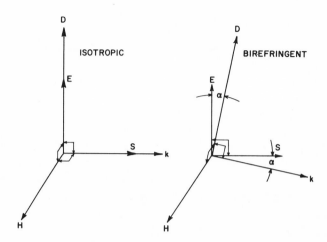

Figure 10. Field, induction, propagation, and energy-transport
vectors in isotropic and in birefringent media.

which is equal to that between **D** and **E**, depends in an involved fashion
on the direction of **D** with respect to the crystal axes, a relationship involving
the various tensor coefficients, which are independent functions of the
frequency.

Suppose we know the frequency and the directions of propagation and
wave polarization of a light beam in a crystal; we then can find the magnitude
of its propagation vector **k**, and thereby its index of refraction, by comparing
Eqs. (134) and (139). Both are relations between **D** and **E**; they must be
consistent. To make the comparison, we equate the components of **D**,
obtaining three simultaneous equations for the components of **E**; form the
determinant of their coefficients; and equate it to zero. The result is a
relation among the components of **k**, the tensor elements of the susceptibility $\chi_{ij}$, and the frequency $\omega$. This is equivalent to a determination of the
index of refraction as a function of the directions of propagation and of
wave polarization, as well as of the frequency. The general relation so
obtained is a dispersion formula, but more complicated than Eq. (51):

$$\left| \omega^2 \mu_0 (\delta_{ij} + \chi_{ij}) - k^2 \delta_{ij} - k_i k_j \right| = 0. \tag{140}$$

Its most interesting property is that it is quadratic in $k$. When the direction of **k** is given (i.e., by specifying the various $k_i/k$), two possible values
of its magnitude result. The two distinct plane wave modes to which these
values correspond propagate at unequal phase velocities, and their **D**-

vectors are polarized in two perpendicular planes.* The corresponding **E**-vectors, however, are not perpendicular except for special cases peculiar to the class of crystal and the special restrictions which its symmetry places on the tensor elements $\chi_{ij}$. Their Poynting vectors also are not in general collinear.

Optics recognizes three classes of crystal: (1) cubic (which are optically isotropic); (2) uniaxial (which includes rhombohedral, tetragonal, and hexagonal lattice types); and (3) biaxial. We shall discuss only the uniaxial type.

In uniaxial crystals, one principal axis of the tensor $\chi_{ij}$ coincides with an axis of symmetry, called the optic axis, of the crystal. The other two principal axes are perpendicular to the optic axis and have equal principal values of the corresponding dielectric tensor. The respective principal values are denoted by $\chi_p$ and $\chi_s$.

Let us take the $x$ axis of a set of rectangular coordinates along the optic axis† of a uniaxial crystal (Figure 11). Equation (135) reduces to

$$\begin{pmatrix} D_x \\ D_y \\ D_z \end{pmatrix} = \begin{pmatrix} 1 + \chi_p & 0 & 0 \\ 0 & 1 + \chi_s & 0 \\ 0 & 0 & 1 + \chi_s \end{pmatrix} \cdot \begin{pmatrix} E_x \\ E_y \\ E_z \end{pmatrix} \tag{141}$$

which must be consistent with the Maxwell equations, Eqs. (136) and (137).

Consider first plane waves propagating along the optic axis. Independent wave polarizations are [Figure 11(a), (b)]

$$
\begin{aligned}
&\text{(a)} \quad \mathbf{k} = \mathbf{x}_1 k, \quad \mathbf{D} = \mathbf{y}_1 D_{0y} \\
&\text{(b)} \quad \mathbf{k} = \mathbf{x}_1 k, \quad \mathbf{D} = \mathbf{z}_1 D_{0z}.
\end{aligned}
\tag{142}
$$

Any other wave polarization contains a mixture of these two components.

Comparing Eqs. (139) and (141),

---

* In practice, one cannot easily reproduce this particular situation of two waves with parallel **k**-vectors unless (1) they have been generated within the medium itself (e.g., in a birefringent laser material), or (2) they originate from a single light beam which enters from outside the medium at normal incidence to the bounding surface. With other directions of incidence, they will be refracted unequally and propagate in distinct directions inside the medium.

† In crystal optics, the term "axis" denotes a preferred *direction*, not merely one line as it does in geometry. It is often made the direction of the $Z$ axis of coordinates, although not universally so. Taking the $Z$ axis in the direction of the crystal optic axis is more common.

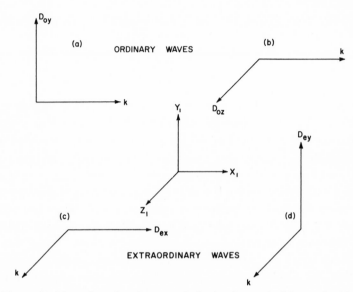

Figure 11. Normal modes of wave polarization in a uniaxial crystal with optic axis in the $X$ direction.

(a)     $D_{0y} = \varepsilon_0(1 + \chi_s)E_y = (k^2/\mu_0\omega^2)E_y$

(b)     $D_{0z} = \varepsilon_0(1 + \chi_s)E_z = (k^2/\mu_0\omega^2)E_z.$

$$\text{(143)}$$

The index of refraction has the same value

$$\nu_0 = kc/\omega = (1 + \chi_s)^{1/2} \tag{144}$$

for either wave polarization when the propagation vector lies along the optic axis. Moreover, $\mathbf{D}$ and $\mathbf{E}$ then have the same directions. This is clearly a consequence of the identity of $\chi_{yy}$ and $\chi_{zz}$.

Now direct the propagation vector normal to the optic axis, say, along $Z$. The two independent wave components of $\mathbf{D}$ are then [Figure 11(c), (d)]

(c)     $\mathbf{k} = \mathbf{z}_1 k,$     $\mathbf{D} = \mathbf{x}_1 D_{ex},$

(d)     $\mathbf{k} = \mathbf{z}_1 k,$     $\mathbf{D} = \mathbf{y}_1 D_{oy},$

$$\text{(145)}$$

and the consistency requirements are

(c)     $D_{ex} = \varepsilon_0(1 + \chi_p)E_x = (k^2/\mu_0\omega^2)E_x,$

(d)     $D_{oy} = \varepsilon_0(1 + \chi_s)E_y = (k^2/\mu_0\omega^2)E_y.$

$$\text{(146)}$$

In this case, different indices of refraction apply to the two waves; respectively,

$$v_e = (1 + \chi_p)^{1/2},$$
$$v_o = (1 + \chi_s)^{1/2}, \tag{147}$$

although in this special case, $\mathbf{D}$ and $\mathbf{E}$ are parallel for each wave polarization.

In the more general case (arbitrary direction of $\mathbf{k}$) analysis is less simple, since $\mathbf{D}$ and $\mathbf{E}$ lie in different directions. However, it can be shown that whenever the susceptibility tensor takes the diagonal form of Eq. (141), two distinct values of the index of refraction will apply, one to each of two mutually perpendicular wave polarizations, for every direction of the propagation vector. These indices are equal only when $\mathbf{k}$ lies along the optic axis. For one of the two wave polarization components ($\mathbf{D}$ normal to $\mathbf{x}_1$), the index of refraction is always $v_0$, the "ordinary" value. The value of the index of refraction applying to the other component of $\mathbf{D}$ lies between $v_0$ and $v_e$. For some crystals, $\chi_s > \chi_p$; for others, the reverse is true. The former are termed positive crystals; the latter, negative (see Figure 12).

In biaxial crystals, all three diagonal members of the susceptibility tensor are different.

For a general representation of the dependence of the index of refraction on the directions of $\mathbf{D}$ and $\mathbf{k}$, it is useful to employ the *reciprocal*

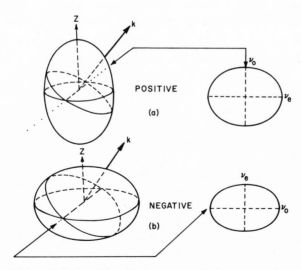

Figure 12. Index ellipsoids for (a) positively and (b) negatively uniaxial crystals, illustrating the construction relating refractive indices to direction of propagation.

dielectric tensor. This may be represented by the equation

$$\varepsilon_{ij}^{-1} x_i x_j = \frac{1}{\varepsilon_0} \left( \frac{x^2}{1 + \chi_{xx}} + \frac{y^2}{1 + \chi_{yy}} + \frac{z^2}{1 + \chi_{zz}} \right) = 1 \qquad (148)$$

if the coordinate axes for $x$, $y$, and $z$ are aligned with the three principal axes of the dielectric tensor. This defines an ellipsoidal surface, called the "index ellipsoid," having the following physical significance: If we specify a direction of propagation of a light wave, i.e., of $\mathbf{k}$, we can describe the two orthogonal normal modes of the electromagnetic field for this direction (and frequency) by passing through the center of the index ellipsoid a plane oriented with its normal in the direction of $\mathbf{k}$. The trace of the index ellipsoid on this plane will always be an ellipse. Its two principal axes lie in the directions of the two normal modes of the electric induction $\mathbf{D}$, and their lengths are the applicable respective values of the index of refraction.

Figure 12 illustrates this construction. Figure 12(a) is the index ellipsoid of a positive crystal, the $Z$ direction being that of the optical axis. Figure 12(b) shows the similar construction for a negative uniaxial crystal.

## 3.6. ZEEMAN AND STARK EFFECTS

In 1896, Zeeman discovered that the immersion of a light source in a magnetic field modifies the spectrum of its emission lines. Later, a similar, inverse effect was observed in absorption spectra. A classical theory of these effects was given by Lorentz shortly after their discovery.

The classical theory correctly describes the normal Zeeman effect, in which each spectrum line is split into a triplet (Figure 13). It assumes the light to be emitted by atomic electrons describing circular orbits about a central positively charged core at angular velocity $\omega_0$. The $\mathbf{v} \times \mathbf{B}$ forces created by this motion in the magnetic field [Eq. (1)] modify the effective central force on the circulating electron.

To an observer at rest in a system of coordinates rotating in the sense of a right-handed screw about the field lines at the (small) angular frequency

$$\omega_L = eB/2m \qquad (149)$$

the extra magnetic force is just compensated by centrifugal force, and the description of the electron's motion is identical with that of the atom at rest in zero magnetic field. This observer sees the normal spectrum.

However, an external observer not sharing in the rotation sees light at the two frequencies which are combinations of the two rotational fre-

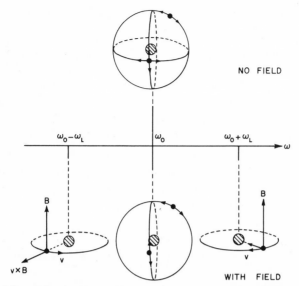

Figure 13. Classical mechanism for the normal Zeeman effect, showing three principal orientations for the orbit plane of an atomic electron with respect to a magnetic field, and the respective directions of magnetic forces which perturb the electron motion.

quencies,

$$\omega = \omega_0 \pm \omega_L, \tag{150}$$

except for the light emitted by those atoms which have their electron orbit planes oriented parallel to the field. Lorentz' analysis showed that one-third of the atoms are effectively so oriented, while, of the remaining two-thirds, one-third rotate in the right-handed sense (to which the plus sign applies), and the other third in the left-handed sense (producing the difference frequency).

This analysis predicts an undisplaced, plane-polarized center line with two equally displaced combination lines both polarized perpendicular to the central line. Viewed along the field direction, only the displaced lines are seen, and they are then circularly polarized in opposite senses. This is observed in spectra having three-component Zeeman patterns.

In many instances, however, the Zeeman line patterns are much more complicated, and the normal triplet appears only as a limiting case with extremely strong magnetic fields. The anomalous Zeeman effect and the Paschen–Back effects, as these phenomena are called, have been quantitatively explained with the quantum theory.

According to the quantum theory, a spectrum line is emitted in a transition between stationary states of the atomic system. The respective energies of these states are found by solving Schrödinger's equation. When a magnetic field is present, Schrödinger's equation has additional terms arising from the interaction of the magnetic field with the magnetic moments of the electron orbits. When the energy of this interaction, which is quantized, is added to each discrete energy value of the unperturbed atom, the original levels are split into a number of discrete sublevels characterized by a set of magnetic quantum numbers. The Zeeman pattern is determined by displacements of both the initial and final groups of sublevels, and by selection rules which include rules for the change of magnetic quantum number in allowed transitions.

Equations (149) and (150) indicate that the actual Zeeman splitting is small. In a field of 10,000 G, or, using mks units, $B = 1$ V-sec/m$^2$, the Larmor frequency is $\omega_L = 0.83(11)$ sec$^{-1}$, only a small fraction of the frequency of the light.

Electric fields also perturb the energy states of an atom, and again quantum-mechanical analysis is needed to determine the splitting. This, the Stark effect, is also very small. The central field to which electrons are bound is approximately

$$E_{\text{atom}} = e/4\pi\varepsilon_0 a_0{}^2 = 5(11) \quad \text{V/m} \tag{151}$$

[where $a_0$ is the Bohr radius, $a_0 = 0.53(-10)$ m]. This is far stronger than possible artificially produced electric fields.

The theory of the Stark effect is more complicated than that of the Zeeman effect. This is because the electric field *creates* a dipole moment in the atom; the magnetic moment of the electron orbit is essentially independent of the applied field.

Both electrooptical and magnetooptical effects are observed in light propagation phenomena. Some magnetooptical effects are directly relatable to the Zeeman splitting; the important electrooptical effects are not directly relatable to the Stark effect, however.

## 3.7. ELECTROSTRICTION AND PIEZOELECTRICITY

Dielectrics are subjected to internal stress when an electric field is applied. The force on a unit volume element within a dielectric is that of the internal field acting on the polarization. If the field intensity is a function of position, a net body force,

$$\mathbf{F} = \mathbf{P} \cdot \nabla \mathbf{E} = (\varepsilon - \varepsilon_0)\mathbf{E} \cdot \nabla \mathbf{E}, \tag{152}$$

is created proportional to the square of the electric field intensity. Just as in the vacuum case, the electrostatic stored energy density can be shown to be $\frac{1}{2}\mathbf{D} \cdot \mathbf{E}$, and the body force is derived from its gradient. In a uniform electric field, there is still stress, taking the form of tension $\frac{1}{2}\varepsilon E^2$ along the field lines and with pressure of equal magnitude normal to the field; a tension $\frac{1}{2}\varepsilon E^2$ is exerted from outside (i.e., from the sources of the field) on the slab.

These electrically generated stresses give rise to mechanical deformation, or strain, creating the opposing stresses which reestablish equilibrium. In those dielectrics which are both electrically and mechanically isotropic, the result of these stresses is an extension along the field direction, termed "electrostriction." The deformation involves density changes, with corresponding changes in $\varepsilon$. The magnitude of the deformation depends not only on the elastic modulus of the medium, but also on the dependence of the dielectric constant on density. This will be discussed further in Section 5.3.2.

Electrostriction does not have an inverse effect in linear isotropic dielectrics, i.e., one cannot generate an electric field simply by applying mechanical pressure. However, there is a large class of solids in which the internal stresses are not strictly proportional to $E^2$, but contain another component directly proportional to $E$. In these bodies, mechanical deformation does give rise to an internal electric polarization proportional to the strain. This polarization arises from unequal displacements of different ion species composing the lattice of the solid. These are termed "piezoelectric" substances.

In these media the relation of induction to field is given by equations of the form

$$D_i = \varepsilon_{ij}E_j + \gamma_{ijk}\sigma_{jk}, \tag{153}$$

one for each component. Summation over repeated indices being understood, a double summation is indicated by the second term. The tensors $\gamma_{ijk}$ and $\sigma_{jk}$ are, respectively, the "piezoelectric tensor" and the "stress tensor." The former characterizes the piezoelectric properties of the substance. The latter characterizes its elastic properties; it allows the components $F_i$ of the body force per unit volume within the dielectric to be calculated from

$$F_i = \partial\sigma_{ij}/\partial x_j. \tag{154}$$

In the usual problem, the constraints or forces on the bounding surfaces, the externally applied electric fields, and the internal stresses then are not independent. They must be found by simultaneous solution of the field equations with the equations of mechanical equilibrium, using known relations between stress and strain and between susceptibility and density for that substance.

The piezoelectric tensor is symmetrical in two of its indices and, in general, may have 18 independent nonvanishing elements. It is a property of third-rank tensors that all elements change sign when the signs of all three coordinates are reversed, an operation equivalent to inversion of the coordinate system about the origin. The components of the piezoelectric tensor must not change sign or magnitude in any symmetry transformation; hence an inversion in a center of symmetry is not allowed. The piezoelectric substances therefore belong to those crystal classes in which the unit cell lacks an inversion center; 20 of the 32 crystal types admit of piezoelectricity.

## 3.8. ELECTRICALLY INDUCED BIREFRINGENCE

It was discovered by Kerr in 1895 that amorphous substances (e.g., glass, many liquids) which are isotropic under ordinary conditions become doubly refracting when subjected to strong electric fields. They then resemble uniaxial crystals with their optic axes parallel to the applied field.

In 1893, Pockels discovered a similar but much weaker effect in several crystals. Isotropic (cubic) crystals become uniaxial, and uniaxial crystals may become biaxial, in a steady electric field of sufficient intensity.

The existence of electrooptical effects requires that the susceptibility tensor be a function of the electric field intensity. The form of this functional dependence can be deduced by recalling that the susceptibility tensor is of rank two. A medium which is isotropic does not provide a vector from which this tensor can be formed in combination with $\mathbf{E}$; moreover, in the Kerr effect, the optic axis is determined solely by the field direction. Hence in an isotropic medium, the susceptibility tensor must be a quadratic function of $\mathbf{E}$. On the other hand, in an anisotropic substance, for which the magnitude of the electrooptical effect depends, not only on the magnitude of $\mathbf{E}$, but also on its orientation with respect to the crystal axes, $\chi$ can contain terms linear in $E$ as well. In general, the susceptibility tensor must be represented by a series expansion in powers of $E$. Odd powers of $E$ do not appear in the susceptibility of isotropic media. Linear optics considers only the constant term.

The birefringence created in a liquid is measured by the Kerr electrooptical constant $J$, defined as the ratio of the relative difference between the two principal refractive indices to the square of the applied electric field intensity which produces it:

$$J = \{\,|\nu_e - \nu_0|\,\}/\nu_0 E^2. \tag{155}$$

The larger organic molecules with side chains show more pronounced Kerr effects. The value of $J$ decreases with increasing temperature. A similar effect is caused by streaming in moving liquids. These facts suggest that the optical anisotropy induced in a liquid results largely from alignment of electrically anisotropic molecules. It can attain full magnitude only in electric fields which vary slowly, so that the molecular dipoles can follow the field, and the alignment is destroyed by thermal agitation, just as in the magnetization of ferromagnetic substances.

In solids, the existence of a linear electrooptical effect requires that the dielectric tensor take the form

$$\varepsilon_{ij} = (1 + \chi_{ij}^{E=0} + \chi_{ijk}E_k)\varepsilon_0. \tag{156}$$

Symmetry requires that

$$\chi_{ijk} = \chi_{ikj}, \tag{157}$$

as in the case of the piezoelectric tensor. The same 20 crystal classes which show piezoelectricity show a linear Pockels effect.

This correspondence does not extend to the magnitudes nor to the signs of the tensor coefficients, however. The piezoelectric tensor coefficients are evaluated at zero or low frequency (rf); the Pockels coefficients are evaluated at optical frequency, where dispersion is important. Moreover, there is an intrinsic difference of character in the phenomena. Piezoelectric effects are caused by displacement of *ions*; the optical susceptibility measures the *electronic* polarizability. Directional constraints on the motion of dispersion electrons are often likely in long or asymmetrical molecules; these often also possess permanent dipole moments which can be aligned by an electric field. Similar directional constraints exist in crystals of certain symmetry classes. When the equilibrium position of the dispersion electrons is changed by applying a static electric field to such a substance, the values of the dielectric tensor elements applicable to an optical-frequency field will take on new values which depend on the respective directions of the various vectors with respect to the molecule or crystal axis, the strength of the applied static field, and the frequency of the light wave. The coefficients applicable to the Pockels effect are commonly tabulated in terms of the reciprocal dielectric tensor (i.e., by reference to the index ellipsoid) rather than the $\chi_{ijk}$ of Eq. (156).

## 3.9. OPTICAL ACTIVITY

Transparent liquids composed of organic molecules having two mirror-image ("stereoisomeric") forms and crystals with unit cells lacking a center of symmetry exhibit a property known as optical activity, manifested by rotation of the plane of wave polarization of light.

We may visualize the mechanism of optical activity with the aid of the classical model of a dispersion electron bound to a position of equilibrium within a three-dimensional potential well. The applied field of the light wave displaces the electron; in some circumstances, constraints on the electron motion are such that this displacement is not strictly transverse, but will carry the electron along the propagation direction as well, and so to points at which the phase, magnitude, and even the direction of $\mathbf{E}$ may differ slightly from their values at the undisplaced position. Since the potential well in a crystal is not necessarily isotropic nor a strictly quadratic function of the displacement, these differences may have a slight effect on the applicable value of the susceptibility.

An accurate expression for the electrical displacement may therefore contain terms involving spatial derivatives of $\mathbf{E}$. Obviously, these terms will be extremely small, since the dimensions of typical unit cells are of the order of one Ångstrom unit, only about $10^{-4}$ of the wavelength of light. Nevertheless, the effect is observable and of considerable practical significance.

One can formally express this new dependence by a tensor relation

$$D_i = \varepsilon_{ij}E_j + \gamma_{ijk}(\partial E_j/\partial x_k), \qquad (158)$$

in which the tensor elements are, as usual, functions of the frequency. Analysis beyond the scope of this presentation shows that the tensor $\gamma_{ijk}$ is antisymmetrical. It vanishes in media having unit cells or molecules which are symmetrical with respect to reflection or rotation. In fluid media composed of unequal populations of two stereoisomers, it does not vanish; consideration of their molecular structure reveals that the dispersion electrons oscillate along helical paths within such molecules. Somewhat similar constraint to helical electron paths accompanies the application of a magnetic field (see below). In optically active substances which are isotropic, the relationship is considerably simplified, since $\varepsilon_{ij}$ reduces to a scalar, and the product containing the third-rank tensor $\gamma_{ijk}$ simplifies to a vector operation, which can be written in component form as

$$D_i = \varepsilon E_i + \gamma(\partial E_j/\partial x_k - \partial E_k/\partial x_j), \qquad (159)$$

or in vector notation as

$$\mathbf{D} = \varepsilon\mathbf{E} + \gamma\bar{\nabla} \times \mathbf{E}. \tag{160}$$

In these media, both the induction and the field are perpendicular to the propagation vector $\mathbf{k}$ (unlike the case of birefringence). Application of the curl operator to a plane wave (exponential notation) leads to the equivalent form

$$\mathbf{D} = \varepsilon\mathbf{E} + i\gamma\mathbf{k} \times \mathbf{E}. \tag{161}$$

The (small) vector $\gamma\mathbf{k}$ is called the "gyration vector."

We shall examine the simple case of plane wave propagation in an optically active isotropic medium. The two normal modes of the wave are then circularly polarized; they propagate together, but the planes containing their electric vectors and $\mathbf{k}$ rotate about $\mathbf{k}$ in opposite senses as the wave advances. It is well known that the addition of two equal vectors rotating oppositely forms a plane-polarized harmonic motion. Moreover, a circularly polarized vibration, represented by a uniformly rotating vector, can also be represented as the resultant of two orthogonal, simple, harmonic plane vibrations in phase quadrature.

A plane-polarized wave incident on an optically active medium is there resolved into two circularly polarized modes. Using the complex exponential notation, we let

$$\mathbf{E} = \mathbf{x}_1 E_0 \exp\{i\omega t\} \tag{162}$$

represent the field of the incident wave at the surface of an optically active medium, in which we have taken the $Z$ direction normal to the surface $z = 0$.

Within the medium the wave has the form

$$\mathbf{E} = (\mathbf{x}_1 + i\mathbf{y}_1)(E_0/2) \exp\{i(\omega t - k_d z)\}$$
$$+ (\mathbf{x}_1 - i\mathbf{y}_1)(E_0/2) \exp\{i(\omega t - k_l z)\}, \tag{163}$$

reducing to Eq. (162) at $z = 0$, but containing two opposite circular components, each the resultant of two orthogonal plane vibrations in quadrature. The first rotates in the sense of a right-handed screw, the second in a left-handed sense, as the wave advances. Their propagation vectors, to be determined in the usual way, both lie along the $Z$ axis; they are distinguished by the subscripts $d$ for dextro and $l$ for levo, appropriate to the respective senses of rotation.

The relationship of $\mathbf{D}$ to $\mathbf{E}$, given by Eq. (161), and the wave propagation relation, Eq. (139), determine two values of **k**. For conciseness, this is presented in tabular form (Table I).

Thus the two circularly polarized components which satisfy the field equations propagate at slightly unequal phase velocities. Their resultant remains a plane-polarized wave, but its plane of polarization rotates about the $Z$ axis as the waves pass through the medium.

The difference in refractive index for right and left circular polarization is the basis of a useful analytical method of organic chemistry. Any carbon compound in which one carbon atom has different elements or radicals

## Table I
## Optical Activity

The field of the incident wave at $z = 0$ is $x_1 E_0 \exp\{i\omega t\}$

Circularly polarized modes

| | | |
|---|---|---|
| Electric vector | $\mathbf{E}_d$ | $\mathbf{E}_l$ |
| Sense of rotation | Right | Left |
| Amplitude | $E_0/2$ | $E_0/2$ |
| Propagation constant | $k_d$ | $k_l$ |

Plane-polarized components

| | | |
|---|---|---|
| In $XZ$ plane | $E_0/2$ | $E_0/2$ |
| In $YZ$ plane | $iE_0/2$ | $-iE_0/2$ |
| $i\gamma k E_y$ | $\gamma k_d E_0/2$ | $-\gamma k_1 E_0/2$ |
| $i\gamma k E_x$ | $i\gamma k_d E_0/2$ | $i\gamma k_1 E_0/2$ |
| $D_x$ | $(\varepsilon + \gamma k_d)(E_0/2)$ | $(\varepsilon - \gamma k_1)(E_0/2)$ |
| $D_y$ | $i(\varepsilon + \gamma k_d)(E_0/2)$ | $i(\varepsilon - \gamma k_1)(E_0/2)$ |

| | | |
|---|---|---|
| Total displacement $\mathbf{D}$ | $(\varepsilon + \gamma k_d)\mathbf{E}_d$ | $(\varepsilon - \gamma k_1)\mathbf{E}_l$ |
| Propagation equation | $\mu_0 \omega^2 (\varepsilon + \gamma k_d) = k_d{}^2$ | $\mu_0 \omega^2 (\varepsilon - \gamma k_1) = k_l{}^2$ |
| Index of refraction | $\nu_d{}^2 = (\varepsilon + \gamma k_d)/\varepsilon_0$ | $\nu_1{}^2 = (\varepsilon - \gamma k_1)/\varepsilon_0$ |
| $\nu_0 = \sqrt{\varepsilon/\varepsilon_0}$ | $\nu_d = \nu_0 \sqrt{1 + (\gamma k_d/\nu_0{}^2\varepsilon_0)}$ | $\nu_l = \nu_0 \sqrt{1 - (\gamma k_1/\nu_0{}^2\varepsilon_0)}$ |
| | $\doteq \nu_0 \sqrt{1 + (\gamma\omega/\nu_0 c\varepsilon_0)}$ | $\doteq \nu_0 \sqrt{1 - (\gamma\omega/\nu_0 c\varepsilon_0)}$ |
| | $\doteq \nu_0[1 + (\gamma\omega/2\nu_0 c\varepsilon_0)]$ | $\doteq \nu_0[1 - (\gamma\omega/2\nu_0 c\varepsilon_0)]$ |
| | $= \nu_0 + (\gamma\omega/2c\varepsilon_0)$ | $= \nu_0 - (\gamma\omega/2c\varepsilon_0)$ |

attached to each of its four valence bonds can occur in either of two mirror-imagine forms (or stereoisomers); one is dextrorotatory, the other levorotatory. The gyration vector is of constant magnitude, and its direction always lies along the propagation vector **k** in those media, so that the above analysis applies.

When the optically active medium is a uniaxial or biaxial crystal, analysis in terms of a gyration vector is not so straightforward; the more general tensor relationship, Eq. (158), applies, and the normal modes are elliptically polarized. However, birefringence is by far the greater effect, in general, and optical activity is not important except in the special case when light propagates along the optic axis. This situation is ordinarily degenerate; optical activity removes the degeneracy. Quartz is a common example of an optically active birefringent crystal.

Optical activity and birefringence are sometimes confused, but their origins and manifestations are quite distinct. Birefringence arises from that part of the susceptibility tensor which relates **D** to **E**; optical activity arises from that part of the susceptibility tensor which relates **D** to a spatial derivative of **E**. In the former, the normal modes of the field are plane-polarized; in the latter, they are elliptically or circularly polarized.

## 3.10. MAGNETOOPTICAL EFFECTS

Application of a magnetic field to certain transparent solids, some of which show no natural optical activity (e.g., glass), causes rotation of the plane of polarization of light propagating along the field lines. Here it is the magnetic field rather than the molecular structure which imparts a twist to the electronic motion. For these media, the gyration vector is proportional and parallel to the magnetic vector **H**. This effect bears the name of Faraday.

The magnitude of the Faraday effect is measured by the factor relating the gyration vector to the field intensity. The most useful relationship is in the form

$$d\theta/dz = \alpha + VH, \tag{164}$$

in which $\theta$ is the angle through which the polarization plane has rotated after passage in the direction of **H** through a thickness $z$; $H$ is the magnetic field intensity; $\alpha$ and $V$ are constants of the medium, the former allowing for natural optical activity. The constant $V$ is termed Verdet's constant. It is usually tabulated in units of angular minutes centimeter$^{-1}$ oersted$^{-1}$. In using this formula, one must take care: reversal of the direction of propagation by reflection cancels natural rotation but doubles the Faraday rotation, since the magnetic gyration vector aligns with **H** rather than with **k**.

The Faraday effect is closely related to the Zeeman effect. An elementary explanation relates it to the Zeeman splitting of an atomic spectral resonance line into $d$- and $l$-circularly polarized components when the line is observed along the direction of the magnetic field. The index of refraction of each component is determined by the value of the respective resonance frequency in accord with the dispersion formula (Section 2.5). These indices differ slightly because the Zeeman effect increases the frequency of one component of the resonance line and reduces that of the other.

Plane-polarized light sent through a gas or simple liquid at a direction normal to an applied magnetic field shows the so-called Voigt effect. The medium appears doubly refracting, the component which is polarized normal to the field forming the extraordinary wave. This effect is also simply explained by reference to the dispersion formula, noting that the normal Zeeman components observed perpendicular to the field are a triplet, the undisplaced center member being polarized parallel to the magnetic vector, and the others polarized normal to it.

Some liquids (e.g., nitrobenzene) show a very large effect, called the Cotton–Mouton effect, under the same circumstances, which cannot be related to the Zeeman effect. Its origin is similar to that of the Kerr electro-optical effect, in that magnetically anisotropic molecules of the liquid align themselves with the magnetic field. The alignment is disturbed by thermal motions, so the effect is temperature-sensitive. Its magnitude is proportional to $H^2$ rather than to the first power of the magnetic field intensity.

## 3.11. FLUORESCENCE AND THE RAMAN EFFECT

The phenomena described in preceding sections of this chapter all concern the dispersion of optical media, and are described by various coefficients the values of which are functions of the frequency. The latter parameter characterizes the light wave, not the medium. It is true that the natural resonance frequencies of the dispersion electrons appear in the dispersion formula, and these frequencies are subject to manipulation, by means of the Zeeman (and Stark) effects; however, in ordinary dispersion phenomena, the natural frequencies of the atom appear only in the formulas, not in the light.

It is well known, however, that *intense* light is not merely absorbed or scattered by many substances, but also excites emission of new spectral lines or bands characteristic of each substance. Ordinarily, but not invariably, this secondary radiation, called fluorescence, is of longer wavelength (lower photon energy) than the exciting radiation (Stokes' law of fluorescence). If the exciting radiation is pulsed, it is sometimes found that the emission of secondary radiation persists for an appreciable time after the primary radiation has been turned off, decaying exponentially with time. The term "phosphorescence" is applied to this phenomenon when the decay is unusually slow, but the quantitative distinction between fluorescence and phosphorescence is not well defined. Moreover, confusion exists concerning the use of the term "fluorescence," some preferring to reserve it for secondary radiation generated by an indirect or incoherent excitation process, and so to distinguish it from the Raman effect. Others use it to embrace all processes obeying Stokes' law, and call only the anti-Stokes phenomena (secondary radiation having *shorter* wavelength than the exciting radiation) the Raman effect.

These phenomena are best described and distinguished with quantum-mechanical models. We have seen in Section 2.5 that an atomic system interacts with radiation by passage through one or more intermediate states. In ordinary dispersion, it passes to the intermediate state and then returns to its initial state by absorption and emission of quanta of exactly equal energy. The entire process is characterized by phase memory, and the two light quanta are coherent.

When the frequency of the light is such that the intermediate state coincides in energy with a stationary state of the atom, the interaction is extremely strong, giving rise to pronounced scattering. This is the case of anomalous dispersion. The scattered light, called resonance radiation, is equal in frequency and is coherent with the incident light. The atom returns to its initial state after the process.

Even if the intermediate state does not coincide with a stationary state, it may be possible for the atom to become excited by the incident radiation. For example, in a gas at high pressure or in the lattice of a solid, nonradiative processes may take up the difference in energy between the radiation-induced state and a slightly lower stationary state of the atom. These processes involve inelastic collisions, and are accompanied by emission of phonons (quanta of sound or lattice vibration). The atom is then left in an excited state; it may decay by spontaneous emission of radiation which, of course, obeys Stokes' law; no phase memory is associated with the spontaneous radiation.

Most solid lasers are pumped by this mechanism; Figure 14 shows the ruby-laser excitation mechanism. The active "atoms" are ions of $Cr^{3+}$

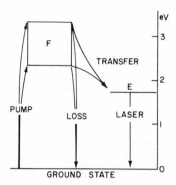

Figure 14. A simplified energy level representation of the excitation mechanism of a
ruby laser.

imbedded in a crystal of $Al_2O_3$. The ions are excited by broadband pump
radiation to state $F$, from which the lattice of $Al_2O_3$ absorbs a small amount
of energy, leaving the $Cr^{3+}$ in state $E$. The $E$ state has a 3-msec mean spontaneous decay time. Under intense pumping irradiation, the population of the
$E$ state can be made to exceed that of the ground state. If the system is
equipped with a mode-selective cavity, stimulated emission deexcites the
$E$ states coherently, drastically reducing their lifetime and producing the
intense laser pulse.

In Raman scattering, the emitted and absorbed quanta are of unequal
energy because the atomic system is left in a different state after the process
terminates; but the two quanta are nevertheless coherent. Since the atom
is usually found in the ground state, the final state of a Raman process is
usually an excited state, and the radiation emitted is of lower energy than
the exciting radiation. This, the Stokes line, is shifted below the exciting
frequency $\omega$ by an amount corresponding to the energy of the final state
$\hbar\omega_1$ (measured from the ground state). Figure 15, corresponding to Figure 7,
depicts these transitions. Radiation of frequency $\omega_1$ may appear at some
subsequent time, although selection rules will probably forbid this or lead
to a very long radiative lifetime for the final state. If no other processes
deexcite the atom, so that its lifetime is indeed long, and if the exciting
radiation is of sufficiently high intensity, it is possible for the excited atom
to interact once again with the radiation field before the excited state has
decayed; again, this interaction takes place by formation of an intermediate
state, followed by a transition to a final state. This latter will usually be
the ground state (Figure 16). Thus it becomes possible for a second line
to appear, which is shifted to frequency $(\omega + \omega_1)$, *higher* than that of the

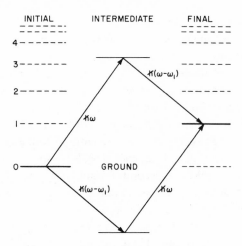

Figure 15. Origin of the Stokes line in Raman
scattering.

exciting light; the energy difference $\hbar\omega_1$ between ground and excited states
is now added to that of the incident quantum $\hbar\omega$. This is the anti-Stokes
line. When the phase memory has not been destroyed by collision, the two
displaced lines are related coherently to the exciting line.

The anti-Stokes line appears only when the intensity of the exciting
line is adequate to establish a perceptible excited-state population. Its
intensity depends on the product of excited-atom concentration and photon

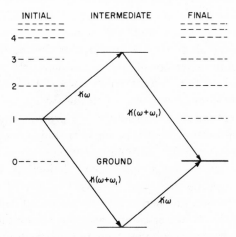

Figure 16. Origin of the anti-Stokes line in
Raman scattering.

flux, and therefore on the square of the exciting intensity. This is *extrinsic* nonlinearity: change in the optical properties of a medium by repopulation of its various states.

On the classical model of dispersion, fluorescent phenomena indicate nonlinear binding of the dispersion electrons to the atom or molecule, but that alone cannot account for fluorescence. It is shown in the Appendix that an oscillator in forced vibration will contain combination frequencies if its potential energy is not strictly a quadratic function of the displacement; however, these new frequencies will be integer multiples of the exciting frequency, unless a second forcing frequency is simultaneously present. We must accordingly assume that the polarization currents induced by a monochromatic wave contain, not only the single frequency of the incident wave, but also new Fourier components at frequencies characteristic of the atom or molecule itself. These are mixed by the nonlinear terms of the susceptibility to give combination (sum and difference) frequencies, i.e., the anti-Stokes and Stokes lines.

The classical explanation of the appearance of a Fourier component in the charge polarization which is not present in the exciting radiation assumes that elastic vibrations of the atoms composing the molecule, at frequency $\omega_1$, are coupled to the electronic vibrations. Only the latter are coupled appreciably to the light wave of frequency $\omega$, but, caused by it to oscillate, transfer energy to the atomic vibration. This is possible if the electron binding forces are not strictly harmonic. The atomic vibration, in turn, causes the electronic susceptibility to vary periodically, so as to frequency-modulate the electronic vibrations. Thus sum and difference components, $\omega + \omega_1$ and $\omega - \omega_1$, appear in the resulting polarization. This explanation does not account for Stokes law, which states that the difference frequency alone should appear, nor for the fact that when it is violated, the anti-Stokes line, $\omega + \omega_1$, is usually relatively weak.

The initial population in the excited state can be adequate to produce an observable anti-Stokes line, even with intense light, only if the direct transition to the ground state is forbidden. The principal interest of spectroscopists in Raman spectra is that it permits the study of energy levels which are not directly excitable by conventional means.

In previous sections, the simple scalar relationship characterizing the linear, isotropic dielectric has been replaced by a tensor relationship containing terms in **E** and in its derivatives, together with dependences on applied magnetic fields. However complicated the relationships involved, the charge polarization possessed the same time dependence as the electric field of the applied wave.

The susceptibility of Raman-active substances also must contain small terms which account for the generation of displaced frequency components. The time-dependence of the charge polarization is then no longer identical with that of the applied wave. The Raman-active medium contains a volume distribution of coherently excited dipoles oscillating at the displaced as well as at the applied frequency, and the complete description of its charge polarization must include them all. The corresponding susceptibility coefficients are functions, not only of frequency, but also of the intensity of the applied field. This is *intrinsic* nonlinearity.

## 3.12. INTENSITY-DEPENDENT OPTICAL PHENOMENA

The existence of the phenomena described in this chapter suggests that practically all classes of optical media should exhibit nonlinear response to sufficiently intense electromagnetic radiation. The most obvious cause of nonlinearity is change in population of the various quantum states of a medium after transitions have been induced by the passing wave. There are more fundamental causes, however, which lead to dependences on the instantaneous intensity of the light. The electrooptical and magnetooptical effects should result, not only from separate application of strong static electric or magnetic fields to dielectric media through which intense light is passing, but also from the electromagnetic fields of light waves. Media which fluoresce or which show the Raman effect must interact in nonlinear fashion if they are to combine their characteristic vibrational frequencies with those of the impressed optical wave. Piezoelectric effects and the Debye–Sears effect demonstrate that light and sound waves can interact; this also requires a nonlinear interaction mechanism.

In general, the phenomena of intrinsic optical nonlinearity involve the replacement of photons at the applied frequency by photons of different frequency generated in interactions with polarizable media. These interactions are adequately described only in quantum-mechanical terms, although considerable progress can be made toward understanding them with the aid of classical models. The propagation of light can be described as that of a classical electromagnetic wave, after the appropriate interaction coefficients have been obtained by quantum-mechanical calculations.

In the remaining chapters of this book, we shall describe the principal intrinsic optical nonlinearity effects, in which the magnitude of the effect is dependent on the intensity of the light.

# 4.

---

# NONLINEAR PHENOMENA
# IN PASSIVE MEDIA

## 4.1. INTRODUCTION

The refractive index, which contains the essential information concerning the macroscopic optical properties of a medium, is usually tabulated as a single number, and for most purposes that is sufficient. A supplementary statement with such a table concerning the reference temperature and wavelength reminds us that $\nu$ is not a constant, but is a function of the density of the medium and of the frequency of the light. When absorption is appreciable, it is necessary to express the index of refraction as a complex number. In birefringent media, there are additional dependences of the index of refraction on the directions of propagation and wave polarization. Careful measurements further reveal weak but significant effects from the application of magnetic and electric fields and of mechanical stress.

The preceding chapter described and related these effects to the microscopic electronic structure of the molecule or unit cell; this treatment led to the conclusion that the index of refraction must also depend slightly on the intensity of the light. These dependences are manifested by the generation of new frequency components.

The complete, exact expression for the index of refraction will therefore be extremely complicated, and it would present a very involved wave propagation problem indeed, were it not for two fortunate circumstances. One can represent the index of refraction by a series of terms, all but the linear term being very small. Moreover, it is often possible to confine attention to only a single additional term of this expansion by special experimental arrangements which allow a chosen process to produce significant effects.*

---

* An example of this was already noted in the previous chapter. The optical activity of quartz is insignificant in comparison with its birefringence, except when the light is

The selected process may usually be treated as a small perturbation the existence of which does not drastically affect the passage of the primary light beam through the medium.

Media which we have termed "passive" do not impose their characteristic frequencies on the light wave. For them, intensity-dependence of the index of refraction may be described by an expansion of the electric susceptibility in powers of the electric field intensity (and of the magnetic field intensity as well, in the case of the Faraday effect). All terms dependent on the optical frequency field intensity lead to creation of optical harmonics, i.e., of light waves at integer multiples of the frequency of the applied light. For these to be observable, however, special arrangements and coherent primary beams of proper intensity are desirable.

Second-harmonic generation can be observed by the use of sensitive spectroscopic techniques with gas-laser sources operating at power levels as low as 1 W. Copious production of second harmonic, on the other hand, requires power densities of the order of 1 MW/cm², specially chosen media in carefully constructed geometries, and a high degree of beam coherence. The onset of stimulated Raman action (Chapter V) in active media at levels of intensity about one order of magnitude higher may be ignored if one is interested solely in harmonic generation, but the threshold of stimulated Brillouin scattering, a destructive process in solids, sets a practical upper limit in the 20–50 MW/cm² range. Third-harmonic generation is easily observable, but is not capable of generating high beam power at primary beam levels within the limit of material damage in solid media. Still higher harmonics are unlikely to be producible, for reasons which will appear in subsequent sections.

The theory of harmonic generation provides the simplest example of the light wave propagation problem in nonlinear media.

## 4.2. ELECTROMAGNETIC WAVES IN NONLINEAR DIELECTRIC: METHOD OF SOLUTION

In Section 2.2, the wave propagation equation was given in a form which reduces to

$$\nabla \times \nabla \times \mathbf{E} + \mu_0 \varepsilon_0 \ddot{\mathbf{E}} + \mu_0 \ddot{\mathbf{P}} = 0. \tag{165}$$

---

directed along the optic axis. It is then the most distinctive property, but there is then no evidence of double refraction.

The charge polarization $\mathbf{P}$ induced by the wave can be written

$$\mathbf{P} = \varepsilon_0 \chi \mathbf{E} + \text{small nonlinear terms.} \qquad (166)$$

Although we solved the wave equation by direct substitution, it was noted in Section 2.2 that this equation can be solved by finding the particular integral contributed by each Fourier component of the polarization and adding it to the solution of the homogeneous wave equation at that frequency. This is interpreted physically as combining the vacuum wave with coherently scattered waves radiated by distributed polarization sources. The result is a similar wave with altered frequency-dependent phase velocity.

The inclusion of the small nonlinear terms of Eq. (166) can be handled by extending the same procedure. The linear part of the polarization term in Eq. (166) is retained in the left side of Eq. (165). The nonlinear parts of the polarization are transferred to the right side; they are regarded as new distributed source terms, contributing additional waves which, to a very good approximation, are superimposed on those of the linear solution. These nonlinear source terms, found by applying the perturbation method to the elementary oscillators of the medium, consist of components at harmonic and mixture frequencies (Appendix). Each of the new wave components to which these sources give rise propagates at a phase velocity not generally equal to that of the fundamental waves. The respective velocities are given by ordinary dispersion theory. This general method will be illustrated in succeeding sections of this chapter.

## 4.3. THE ROLE OF COHERENCE IN HARMONIC GENERATION

### 4.3.1. Superposition of Waves in a Hypothetical Medium with Second-Harmonic Non Linearity. For simplicity, we shall consider the hypothetical case of a semiinfinite medium in which the susceptibility is field-dependent:

$$\chi = \chi_1 + \chi_2 E, \qquad (167)$$

the coefficient $\chi_2$ being of such magnitude that at all practically attainable values of $E$, the second term remains a small perturbation. Both coefficients are functions of the frequency. In general, $\chi_2$ must be a tensor coefficient, a complication we shall conveniently ignore for the moment. Substituting in Eq. (166), we find that the charge polarization,

$$P = P_1 + P_2 = \varepsilon_0(\chi_1 E + \chi_2 E^2), \qquad (168)$$

contains a second-order term $P_2$ proportional to the square of $E$. The wave equation (165) can be written in scalar form as

$$\nabla^2 E + \varepsilon_0\mu_0(1 + \chi_1)\ddot{E} = -\mu_0\ddot{P}_2$$
$$= -\varepsilon_0\mu_0\chi_2\,\partial^2(E^2)/\partial t^2 \tag{169}$$

(where we overlook the possibility that the nonlinear part of the charge polarization may not be in the same direction as **E**).

A monochromatic plane wave of frequency $\omega_1$ introduced into this medium from the plane $z = 0$ (of indefinite extent in the $XY$ plane) can be a solution only of the homogeneous equation; i.e., the wave [see Eq. (25)]

$$E_1 = \tfrac{1}{2}E_0 \exp i\{\omega_1 t - k_1 z\} + \text{comp. conj.} \tag{170}$$

is only the first-order solution of Eq. (169). It is nevertheless a good approximation to the total field for evaluation of the second term of Eq. (167). Using it, one finds that the second-order nonlinearity creates a component of $P$ varying at twice the fundamental frequency, as though another wave were present for which the argument of the exponential is twice that in Eq. (170),

$$E_1^2 = E_0^2(\tfrac{1}{2} + \exp 2i\{\omega_1 t - k_1 z\}). \tag{171}$$

We shall consider the constant term when we discuss optical rectification.

The double-frequency component in the nonlinear polarization is the principal part of the source term $-\mu_0\ddot{P}_2$ of Eq. (169). Thus it is approximately true that

$$\mu_0\ddot{P}_2 = \mu_0\varepsilon_0\chi_2\,\partial^2(E_1^2)/\partial t^2$$
$$= -4\varepsilon_0\mu_0\chi_2\omega_1^2 E_0^2[\exp 2i\{\omega_1 t - k_1 z\}+\text{comp. conj.}] \tag{172}$$

is the distributed source at depth $z$ in the medium. This radiates new waves at the second harmonic of the introduced frequency; these waves, propagating from their uniformly distributed points of origin at the phase velocity corresponding to the harmonic frequency, combine to produce a resultant amplitude at, say, $z = z_0$, which depends on the phase relationships of the various wave components reaching $z_0$.

A simple graphical representation of these internal sources (Figure 17) suggests that in general the new waves generated by the internal harmonic source are not directly additive; their resultant amplitude eventually reaches

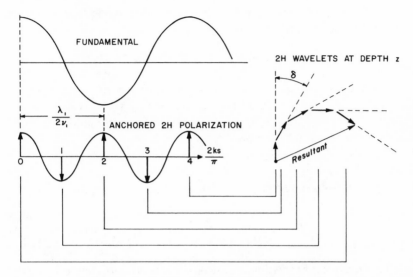

δ = Phase at Source - Phase Equivalent of (z-s) for 2H

Figure 17. Vectorial combination of wavelets from a distribution of nonlinear polarization sources excited by a plane wave.

a maximum and afterward decreases as the thickness of the medium is progressively increased. Analysis confirms this.

The harmonic generated at depth $z = s$ in an infinitesimal slab of thickness $ds$ is

$$q \, ds \exp 2i\{\omega_1 t - k_1 s\}, \tag{173}$$

where we have, for simplicity, dropped the conjugate term.

The simple factor $q$, a (possibly complex) function of the fundamental frequency, containing the phase and source strength of the nonlinear local polarization, replaces the product of factors in Eq. (172). Note that except for the possibility of a (constant) phase factor in $q$, the phase of the local source is determined by the phase of the fundamental wave through its propagation constant $k_1$. The harmonic radiation propagates as a wave of frequency $\omega_2 = 2\omega_1$ and of propagation constant $k_2$ ($\neq 2k_1$, in general). Hence, neglecting absorption, the harmonic generated at depth $s$ reaches depth $z$ as the wavelet

$$dE_2 = q \, ds \exp 2i\{\omega_1 t - k_1 s\} \exp i\{k_2(s - z)\}, \tag{174}$$

the second factor taking account of the phase difference introduced by the optical thickness of the intervening layer. By rearranging the exponential terms, (172) can be rewritten as

$$dE_2 = q \, ds \exp i\{2\omega_1 t - k_2 z\} \exp i\{(k_2 - 2k_1)s\}. \tag{175}$$

The total harmonic radiation at depth $z$ is the vector sum of contributions $dE_2$ arising from all intermediate depths $0 < s < z$. The second exponential factor of Eq. (175) contains the phase information needed to perform this vectorial addition.

The total second harmonic amplitude at the depth $z$ is

$$E_2 = q \exp i\{2\omega_1 t - k_2 z\} \int_0^z \exp i\{(k_2 - 2k_1)s\} \, ds$$

$$= q\left[\frac{1 - \exp i\{(k_2 - 2k_1)z\}}{i(2k_1 - k_2)}\right] \exp i\{2\omega_1 t - k_2 z\}. \tag{176}$$

The equivalent expression in real variables is proportional to $1 - \cos\{(k_2 - 2k_1)z\}$.

### 4.3.2. The Coherence Length and Index Matching.

Ordinarily, since $k_2 \neq 2k_1$, not all contributions to $E_2$ arrive in phase. The factor in braces, $[1 - \exp i\{(k_2 - 2k_1)z\}]/i(2k_1 - k_2)$, representing the beat between two waves of unequal spatial period, is subject to periodic fluctuation of amplitude between zero and a maximum as $z$ increases. The distance

$$Z_c = \pi/\{\,|k_2 - 2k_1|\,\} \tag{177}$$

at which the amplitude factor first reaches its maximum is called the "coherence length." Recalling Eq. (51) and (52), we write

$$k_1 = \nu_1 \omega_1/c \tag{178}$$

and

$$k_2 = 2\nu_2 \omega_1/c; \tag{179}$$

using Eq. (56), the coherence length may then be expressed in terms of the fundamental wavelength $\lambda_1$ and the refractive indices $\nu_1$ and $\nu_2$ of fundamental and second harmonic:

$$Z_c = \lambda_1/\{4\,|\,\nu_2 - \nu_1\,|\,\}. \tag{180}$$

The coherence length is therefore generally only a few wavelengths at most, unless the indices of refraction happen to be almost precisely equal. In the ideal ("index-matched") case of exact equality, the second-harmonic intensity is not limited by interference and the coherence length is infinite. This case will be considered in a later section.

Similar considerations apply, of course, to third-harmonic nonlinearity.

Because of dispersion $\nu_2 \neq \nu_1$ in normal substances. Anomalous dispersion, birefringence, or optical activity must be employed for index matching. The first necessarily involves strong absorption, and the third is rarely large enough to compensate for dispersion, so that harmonic generation is practically confined to plane-polarized light in birefringent media.

These considerations can be demonstrated experimentally by observing the second harmonic generated by laser radiation in a flat slab. By varying the slab's inclination to the laser beam axis, its effective optical thickness is varied (Figure 18). The second-harmonic intensity is then found to vary periodically between zero and a maximum value, being zero whenever the optical thickness is an even multiple of the coherence length and maximum at every odd multiple thereof. This technique is useful for measuring the relevant tensor quantities when used with polarized light and various orientations of the optic axis (see Section 4.4.2).

In ferroelectric crystals, containing anisotropic domains of various orientations, the second harmonic can build up without special provision for index matching; random phase discontinuities at interfaces between domains destroy the coherence between incoming and locally generated harmonic which would otherwise lead to destructive interference. The maximum effect occurs when the domain size is comparable with the

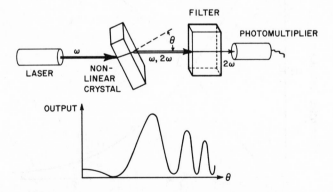

Figure 18. Effect of varying the optical thickness of a nonlinear crystal on generation of the second harmonic of a laser beam. Maxima occur when the effective thickness is an even number of coherence lengths.

coherence length; it is very sensitive to temperature changes and to static applied electric fields.

### 4.3.3. Growth of Second Harmonic in an Index-Matched Medium.
In an index-matched nonlinear medium, the second-harmonic wave field will grow steadily in amplitude as a result of in-phase addition of contributions from each thickness element. Thus we can write

$$dE^{(2\omega)}/dz = C(E^{(\omega)})^2 \tag{181}$$

for the growth of second harmonic $E^{(2\omega)}$ from the fundamental $E^{(\omega)}$, where $C$ is a constant of the medium.

The total energy flux in the radiation will remain constant in a non-absorbing medium, the energy simply being redistributed in frequency.

The total energy flux is, by Eq. (57),

$$\mathbf{S} = \mathbf{E} \times \mathbf{H}$$
$$= [(E^{(\omega)})^2 + (E^{(2\omega)})^2]\varepsilon_0 \nu c/2, \tag{182}$$

so that

$$(E^{(\omega)})^2 + (E^{(2\omega)})^2 = 2S/\varepsilon_0 \nu c = A^2, \tag{183}$$

also a constant. Combining, we find that

$$dE^{(2\omega)}/dz = C[A^2 - (E^{(2\omega)})^2], \tag{184}$$

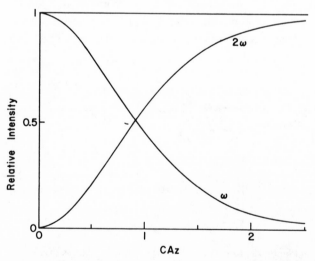

Figure 19. Transfer, as a function of depth, of energy to the harmonic ($2\omega$) from a fundamental beam ($\omega$) in the ideal case of single-mode fundamental and exactly matched refractive indices.

which integrates to

$$E^{(2\omega)} = A \tanh\{CAz\}, \tag{185}$$

with the initial condition $E^{(2\omega)}(z = 0) = 0$.

The fundamental amplitude is then found by subtraction,

$$E^{(\omega)} = A \operatorname{sech}\{CAz\}. \tag{186}$$

Figure 19 illustrates these dependences.

Thus it is theoretically possible for practically complete conversion to occur despite the depletion of the fundamental wave, provided the medium can remain perfectly index matched over sufficiently great depths.

The coefficient $C$ will be determined in later sections.

## 4.4. THE NONLINEAR SUSCEPTIBILITY TENSOR

### 4.4.1. Classical Mechanism. 
The preceding sections dealt with a hypothetical isotropic medium; the tensor character of the dielectric susceptibility was ignored in order to clarify the discussion of the important role of coherence. Actually, second-order optical nonlinearity is forbidden in isotropic media. The classical explanation for this is suggested by Figure 20, which greatly exaggerates the $P$ vs $E$ relationships of two kinds of nonlinear media. In Figure 20(a), the charge polarization changes sign but not magnitude when the field is reversed; its expansion in powers of $E$ must contain only odd terms (i.e., the susceptibility contains only *even* powers of $E$). The medium in Figure 20(b) exhibits a change of magnitude as well as of the sign of $P$ when $E$ is reversed; its dispersion electrons can be displaced in the positive sense more readily than in the negative (these senses being characteristic of the medium); this medium necessarily is optically anisotropic. The expansion of $P$ contains even powers of $E$, but the coefficients depend on the direction of $\mathbf{E}$ and thus on the wave polarization and direction of propagation in the medium of Figure 20(b).

Note, however, that the symmetry of the medium of Figure 20(a) can be destroyed by external application of a static electric field, which displaces the equilibrium position for the dispersion electrons to a new point along the $P(E)$ curve not at the origin, so that the optical frequency polarization will then not behave symmetrically with respect to reversal of the optical electric field.

A necessary physical condition for the existence of even-order nonlinearity, the case in Figure 20(b), is the absence of a center of symmetry

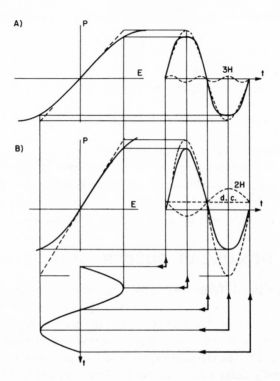

Figure 20. The distinction between odd and even orders of optical nonlinearity. In the former, curve (a), shown by media with inversion symmetry, the relation of polarization to field is symmetrical and only odd harmonics can be generated. Where $P$ is not symmetrically related to $E$, as in curve (b), SHG and rectification are possible. This is shown by the respective waveforms of the polarizations created by a sinusoidal applied electric field.

in the unit cell. This is the same condition as for piezoelectricity. Note, however, that the dispersion *electrons* are directly involved in the optical behavior; it is the displacement of *ions* which gives rise to piezoelectricity. The correspondence is only qualitative.

Figure 20 also illustrates the way in which a second harmonic component can exist in the charge polarization of the medium of Figure 20(b), but not in that of the medium of Figure 20(a), when a purely sinusoidal field (i.e., a monochromatic light wave) is present. Both media can generate the third harmonic, however.

Although useful for clarifying the basic mechanism of optical harmonic generation, Figure 20 oversimplifies the physical situation. We have seen in Chapter 3 that since the dispersion electrons are bound in three-dimensional potential fields shaped according to the structure of the molecule or crystal unit cell, the dependence of **P** on **E** is, in general, a tensor relationship; it could not be displayed in the simple graphical form of Figure 20 even if it were linear. Not only must the direction of **E** be specified before one can describe the resultant charge displacements, but the latter are not necessarily in the same direction as the force which creates them.

Moreover, in the analysis of **P(E)** into harmonics of a fundamental frequency, it is not only possible, but likely, that the directions of the various harmonic components of **P** are different. A plane-polarized fundamental can generate second harmonic which is polarized in a different plane. It is sometimes possible to separate the two frequencies without the use of filters by taking advantage of their distinct directions of wave polarization.

## 4.4.2. Susceptibility Tensors for Optical Harmonic Generation.
The essential feature for second-harmonic generation (SHG) is the existence of a perceptible dependence of the electronic polarization on the square of the electric field intensity at optical frequencies, in addition to the usual direct dependence.

Practically all SHG materials are birefringent crystals. When its SHG is under consideration, the $i$th component of the total charge polarization **P** in a birefringent medium contains two contributions

$$P_i = P_i^{(\omega)} + P_i^{(2\omega)}, \qquad i = 1, 2, 3, \tag{187}$$

where

$$P_i^{(\omega)} = \varepsilon_0 \chi_{ij}^{(\omega)} E_j^{(\omega)} \qquad i, j = 1, 2, 3 \tag{188}$$

and

$$P_i^{(2\omega)} = \varepsilon_0 \chi_{ijk}^{(2\omega)} E_j^{(\omega)} E_k^{(\omega)}, \qquad i, j = 1, 2, 3. \tag{189}$$

The first contribution, $P_i^{(\omega)}$, already discussed in Section 2.2, accounts for the linear part of the medium's response. The second, $P_i^{(2\omega)}$, is quadratic in the electric field, and introduces the third-rank tensor $\chi_{ijk}^{(2\omega)}$. The superscripts $(\omega)$ and $(2\omega)$ have now become necessary for distinguishing the frequencies at which the respective quantities must be evaluated. Thus two sinusoidal electric field components at frequency $\omega$ acting in combination exert a resultant containing the double frequency $2\omega$ (and a dc term, not required at the moment). The susceptibility factor $\chi_{ijk}$ applicable to their combined effect must be evaluated at the combination frequency. This complication we owe to dispersion. Both subscripts, designating direction, and superscripts, distinguishing frequency, will be needed in the remainder of this book.

Each of the equations (187), (188), and (189) stands for three equations, one for each orthogonal component of the vector **P**. A more condensed form is often seen:

$$\mathbf{P}^{(2\omega)} = \varepsilon_0 \boldsymbol{\chi}^{(2\omega)} : \mathbf{E}^{(\omega)}\mathbf{E}^{(\omega)}, \tag{190}$$

which must be interpreted as equivalent to Eq. (189).

Equation (189) accounts only for the second-harmonic component of the charge polarization created by a monochromatic fundamental. As this wave progresses into the medium, it becomes admixed with its harmonic; the latter also contributes to the total charge polarization at the double frequency. Then Eq. (189) must be supplemented by an additional term, formally like the right-hand side of Eq. (188) except for its superscripts.

Some examples of the second-order susceptibility tensor are given in Table II. Writing in this form, which avoids the problem of presenting a cubic array of $3 \times 3 \times 3$ quantities, is possible because Eq. (189) is

## Table II

| $i$ | $j, k$ | | | | | |
|---|---|---|---|---|---|---|
| | $x, x$ | $y, y$ | $z, z$ | $y, z$ | $x, z$ | $x, y$ |
| Barium titanate | | | | | | |
| $x$ | 0 | 0 | 0 | 0 | $d_{15}$ | 0 |
| $y$ | 0 | 0 | 0 | $d_{15}$ | 0 | 0 |
| $z$ | $d_{31}$ | $d_{31}$ | $d_{33}$ | 0 | 0 | 0 |
| Potassium di-hydrogen phosphate (or "KDP") | | | | | | |
| $x$ | 0 | 0 | 0 | $d_{14}$ | 0 | 0 |
| $y$ | 0 | 0 | 0 | 0 | $d_{14}$ | 0 |
| $z$ | 0 | 0 | 0 | 0 | 0 | $d_{36}$ |
| Quartz | | | | | | |
| $x$ | $d_{11}$ | $-d_{11}$ | 0 | $d_{14}$ | 0 | 0 |
| $y$ | 0 | 0 | 0 | 0 | $-d_{14}$ | $-2d_{11}$ |
| $z$ | 0 | 0 | 0 | 0 | 0 | 0 |

indifferent to the order in which the two electric field intensities are taken, only their product having significance. Piezoelectric tensor coefficients are also given in this form.

The numerical values of the tensor coefficients, represented by the letter $d$, are functions of frequency and temperature; only isolated values are known. Moreover, solid-phase transitions, in which the unit cell is rearranged, can change even the forms of these tensors, which are given for the room-temperature configurations.

Notice also that the units of $\chi_{ijk}^{(2\omega)}$ are not the same as those of $\chi_{ij}^{(\omega)}$. The first-order linear susceptibility $\chi_{ij}^{(\omega)}$ is a dimensionless ratio, independent of the system of units in which measured values of $P$ and $E$ are expressed. The values of coefficients in the second-order susceptibility tensor $\chi_{ijk}^{(2\omega)}$, which describes the nonlinearity, are *not* independent of the system of units; they have dimensions inverse to those of electric field intensity. Thus in mks units, the second-order susceptibility is in meters/volt; in cgs units, it is in esu/dyne. The rationalized mks unit is therefore larger than the unrationalized cgs unit of second-order susceptibility by the factor

$$4\pi \text{ (meter/centimeter)(coulomb/esu)(erg/joule)} = 12\pi (4).$$

### 4.4.3. Calculation of the Nonlinear Susceptibility.

Quantum-mechanically, the generation of second harmonic consists in the replacement of two photons each of energy $\hbar\omega_1$ by a single photon of energy $\hbar 2\omega_1 = \hbar\omega_2$ in a coherent interaction of electrons in the crystal cell with the electromagnetic field. For this virtual absorption–reemission process, the system must pass through one of two possible intermediate states, one formed by absorption of two photons of energy $\hbar\omega_1$, the other by emission of one photon of energy $2\hbar\omega_1$.

The expectation value of the second-order nonlinear susceptibility is calculable by standard methods of time-dependent perturbation theory carried to second order. The charge polarization of the dielectric is the expectation electric dipole moment per unit volume; thus if $\mathbf{r}$ is the displaced position of a dispersion electron and $\psi$ is the ground state wave function normalized to the number of atoms per unit volume,

$$\mathbf{P} = \langle \psi_g \mid e\mathbf{r} \mid \bar{\psi}_g \rangle. \tag{191}$$

Unless there are permanent dipoles, this vanishes in the absence of a field.

To determine magnitude of the charge polarization created by a light wave, one notes that the wave functions $\psi_g$ are perturbed by the electromagnetic field; the latter is represented by an interaction term in the Hamiltonian, approximately $\mathbf{A} \exp\{i\mathbf{k} \cdot \mathbf{r}\}$, as noted in Section 2.5.2. The perturbed wave function is written as an expansion in terms of the unperturbed eigenstates of the system,

$$\psi_g{}' = \Sigma \, a_n \psi_n, \tag{192}$$

in which the coefficients $a_n$ are functions of the time; they are found by substitution in Schrödinger's equation with the initial condition that the atomic systems are in their ground states,

$$a_n(t = 0) = \delta(n, g). \tag{193}$$

The values of the $a_n$ after long times allow one to calculate $\mathbf{P}$, and, knowing $\mathbf{E}$, the susceptibility.

The appropriate matrix elements and wave functions are those which apply to unit cells of the crystal lattice, rather than to isolated atoms. Their calculation requires an integration over the unit cell, using Bloch wave functions for the electrons. The result has nonvanishing terms of even order in the field intensity only when the unit cell lacks inversion symmetry, or when a static electric field is also present.

The coefficients which apply to dc-induced second-harmonic generation may be calculated by adding to the perturbing term of the Hamiltonian a term of the form $-e\mathbf{E}^{(0)} \cdot \mathbf{r}$, where $\mathbf{E}^{(0)}$ is the dc electric field.

Each order of the nonlinear susceptibility is found by extracting terms of that order in $\mathbf{E}$ from the expectation value of the charge polarization, the calculation being carried to the corresponding order in perturbation theory.

In Section 3.8, Eq. (156), we noted that the Pockels electrooptical effect requires a symmetrical third-rank tensor to characterize the dielectric constant. The same tensor is involved in optical second-harmonic generation, but, owing to dispersion, the individual tensor coefficients do not necessarily have the same values as for the Pockels effect. They must be calculated as shown above, or measured at the appropriate frequency.

## 4.5. TRAVELING-WAVE SECOND-HARMONIC GENERATION

We now turn from the simplified pictures of earlier sections to the much more complicated general problem of SHG, in which the interactions between the respective waves are represented by tensor elements of the susceptibility. The algebraic complexity of the general situation compels us still to describe simple cases rather than to develop a general analysis, with the objective of making it possible for the reader to use the very detailed literature on the subject, rather than of providing a substitute therefor.

The propagation problem is one of finding consistent wave solutions of two coupled partial differential equations for the field vectors $\mathbf{E}^{(\omega)}$ and $\mathbf{E}^{(2\omega)}$ given initial conditions on the amplitudes and the directions of propagation and wave polarization of each wave.

Equation (165) is first written for each of the two frequency components. These may be further resolved into space components. Each resulting propagation equation contains a coupling term arising from nonlinear response to a sum or difference of two waves. Thus in the equation for the $i$ component of the second harmonic, the coupling term is given by Eq. (189), the fields $E_j^{(\omega)}$ and $E_k^{(\omega)}$ combining to produce their sum frequency $2\omega$ in the charge polarization. Similarly, in the fundamental equation, a nonlinear coupling term having the form $\chi_{ijk}^{(\omega)}E_j^{(2\omega)}E_k^{(\omega)}$ appears because the *difference* frequency of harmonic and fundamental is equal to the fundamental frequency.* The latter term is very small unless the second-harmonic wave has accumulated some intensity, but it must be included in the general analysis.

The propagation equations are therefore

$$c^2(\nabla \times \nabla \times \mathbf{E}^{(\omega)})_i = \omega^2[E_i^{(\omega)} + \chi_{ij}^{(\omega)}E_i^{(\omega)} + \chi_{ijk}^{(\omega)}E_j^{(\omega)}E_k^{(2\omega)}] \qquad (194)$$

for the fundamental, and

$$c^2(\nabla \times \nabla \times \mathbf{E}^{(2\omega)})_i = (2\omega)^2[E_i^{(2\omega)} + \chi_{ij}^{(2\omega)}E_j^2 + \chi_{ijk}^{(2\omega)}E_j^{(\omega)}E_k^{(\omega)}], \qquad (195)$$

for the second-harmonic wave fields.

The complete solutions of these equations can be regarded as combinations of both freely propagating and forced waves. Were the nonlinear coupling terms absent, each equation would describe a freely-propagating wave: the fundamental would have the familiar $\exp i\{\omega t - \mathbf{k}_1 \cdot \mathbf{r}\}$ dependence, and the harmonic[†] would have the wave factor $\exp i\{2\omega t - \mathbf{k}_2 \cdot \mathbf{r}\}$. Each of the coupling terms creates in the charge polarization sources of radiation with spatial distribution determined by the other wave. Thus in the harmonic-frequency component of $\mathbf{P}$, there is a dependence

$$[\exp i\{\omega t - \mathbf{k}_1 \cdot \mathbf{r}\}]^2 = \exp i\{2\omega t - 2\mathbf{k}_1 \cdot \mathbf{r}\}$$

---

\* The difference arises from the product of one of the wave factors with the conjugate of the other. We are not interested in the sum, which is a third harmonic.
† Obviously having been produced in a different medium.

which is *not* that of the freely-propagating harmonic *unless* the index-match condition is exactly fulfilled. It is said to be "anchored to the fundamental wave."

It is not necessary in general that the two wave propagation vectors be collinear, although that situation is the most important case. We shall later turn to the question of noncollinear waves. For the present, we confine discussion to the traveling-wave interaction in which the waves share a common direction of propagation.

Once again, to clarify the argument, an oversimplified situation will be examined, in which only the diagonal terms of the two susceptibility tensors do not vanish, so both waves are polarized in the same plane. We take the $Z$ axis in the direction of propagation and the wave polarization in the $X$ direction. If we try as solutions

$$\mathbf{E}^{(\omega)} = \mathbf{x}_1 \cdot \tfrac{1}{2}E_1(z)[\exp i\{\omega t - k_1 z\} + \exp - i\{\omega t - k_1 z\}] \qquad (196)$$

and*

$$\mathbf{E}^{(2\omega)} = -\mathbf{x}_1 \cdot (i/2)E_2(z)[\exp i\{2\omega t - k_2 z\} + \exp -i\{2\omega t - k_2 z\}], \quad (197)$$

then the coupling terms contain the following factors, respectively:

$$(E^{(\omega)}E^{(2\omega)}) = (-i/4)E_1 E_2[\exp i\{\omega t - (k_2 - k_1)z\} + \exp -i\{\omega t - (k_2 - k_1)z\}], \qquad (198)$$

$$(E^{(\omega)}E^{(\omega)})^{(2\omega)} = \tfrac{1}{4}E_1{}^2[\exp i\{2\omega t - 2k_1 z\} + \exp - i\{2\omega t - 2k_1 z\}]. \qquad (199)$$

The index-matching condition,

$$k_2 = 2k_1 \qquad (200)$$

further simplifies the ensuing algebra, since its fulfillment gives to each equation the same wave factors in all terms. If Eq. (200) is not fulfilled, Eq. (196) then contains a second, forced wave with $k_2$ in its argument, as noted above, and a similar amendment must be made to Eq. (197).

Note that the amplitude factors $E_1$ and $E_2$ are both undetermined functions of $z$. In the two successive differentiations required to evaluate the double curl operator, derivatives are taken of these amplitudes as

---

* Observe that there is a phase shift factor of $\exp -\{i\pi/2\} = -i$ in the amplitude of the harmonic wave. If this assumption is not made, the imaginary factor $i$ will appear in Eqs. (204) and (205). It is preferable to assume it at the outset.

well as of the wave factors. Applying this operation to the right side of Eq. (196) leads to

$$\mathbf{\nabla} \times \mathbf{\nabla} \times \mathbf{E} = \mathbf{x}_1\left[k_1{}^2E_1 + 2ik_1\frac{dE_1}{dz} - \frac{d^2E_1}{dz^2}\right] \cdot (\text{wave factor } \omega, k), \quad (201)$$

with an exactly similar result for the harmonic, except for its wave factor.

The second derivatives of the slowly varying amplitudes we shall neglect.

The index-matched amplitude equations then become, respectively,

$$k_1{}^2E_1 + 2ik_1\frac{dE_1}{dz} = \frac{\omega^2}{c^2}\left[(1 + \chi_{11}^{(\omega)})E_1 - i\chi_{111}^{(\omega)}E_1E_2\right] \quad (202)$$

and

$$ik_1{}^2E_2 + ik_1\frac{dE_2}{dz} = \frac{\omega^2}{c^2}\left[i(1 + \chi_{11}^{(2\omega)})E_2 + \chi_{111}^{(2\omega)}E_1{}^2\right]. \quad (203)$$

Introducing the dispersion relations for the common index of refraction $\nu$ corresponding to Eq. (178) and (179), we are left with

$$dE_1/dz = -\omega\chi_{111}^{(\omega)}E_1E_2/2\nu c \quad (204)$$

and

$$dE_2/dz = \omega\chi_{111}^{(2\omega)}E_1{}^2/2\nu c. \quad (205)$$

These equations should be compared with the results of Section 4.3.3, Eqs. (185) and (186); those equations were derived from the principle of constant total energy flow, with the assumption that the fundamental and second harmonic account for all the radiation intensity. It is noteworthy that these results are completely consistent only if $\chi_{111}^{(\omega)} = \chi_{111}^{(2\omega)}$, which need not be generally true. This slight discrepancy arises from the neglect of absorption, which is an inevitable accompaniment of dispersion (Section 3.2). If instead we overlook the frequency dependence of the nonlinear susceptibility, we can identify the constants of proportionality in Eqs. (181)–(186) as

$$C = \pi\chi_{NL}/\nu\lambda \quad (206)$$

and

$$A = E_1(z = 0). \quad (207)$$

Those readers who are already familiar with the theory of traveling-wave amplifiers will recognize its formal similarity to this problem. The nonlinear dielectric constitutes a traveling-wave amplifier, the coupling of the two waves being such that energy initially present only in the fundamental wave is progressively transferred to the other as they advance. The constancy of total energy flow invoked above is analogous to the Manley–Rowe relations of parametric amplifier theory.

Practical situations introduce several complications. The above analysis assumes simple monochromatic plane waves. Truly single-mode laser beams are realized only with great difficulty, and when focused to high intensity, are of much more complicated form than Eq. (196). The interaction terms must include all products of the various field components, including those in which different modes appear together. Other practical complications will be considered in the next section.

## 4.6. INDEX MATCHING IN BIREFRINGENT MATERIALS

Efficient production of optical harmonics has been accomplished only with birefringent SHG materials. This is not merely because such media are apt to have relatively large second-order nonlinear coefficients, but also because the tensor character of these coefficients is such that the index matching requirement, Eq. (200), can be satisfied in some cases.

We have seen that dispersion ordinarily prevents the matching of phase of the freely-propagating second-harmonic with the anchored nonlinear charge polarization which is essential to sustained amplification.

Birefringent crystals have the peculiar property that, although their nonlinear sources are anchored to the fundamental wave which excites them, in these crystals the direction of harmonic-wave polarization may not in general agree with that of the fundamental. This allows one to exploit birefringence so as to compensate dispersion in certain fortuitous cases.

In Figure 21, the vector $z$ has the direction of the optic axis of a uniaxial birefringent crystal. The propagation vector $k$ of a light wave is also shown, directed at an angle $\theta$ with the optic axis. The dashed line, $OO'$, representing a direction normal to the plane containing $z$ and $k$, is that of ordinary wave polarization (an extraordinary wave would have its $D$-vector in the $(z, k)$ plane). We take $X$ and $Y$ coordinate axes at $45°$ to $OO'$ in the plane normal to $Z$.

In the special case $\theta = 0$, the situation becomes degenerate, in that there is then no distinction between the $O$- and $E$-wave polarizations. For $\theta \neq 0$, however, they have slightly unequal phase velocities. Moreover, owing to the tensor character of even the linear charge polarization, the directions of electric field $E$ and induction $D$ do not exactly coincide, so that $k$ is not precisely perpendicular to $E$ nor in precisely the same direction as that of energy propagation. The difference is small; the point is not

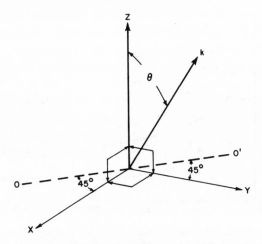

Figure 21. Coordinate system used for calculating SHG in birefringent crystals. The optical axis is in the $Z$ direction. The $X$ and $Y$ axes make equal angles with the plane of incidence and with its normal, $OO'$.

important in the following discussion, so we shall ignore it for simplicity.

For definiteness, we suppose the crystal to be KDP, a commonly used SHG material. It is negatively birefringent, transparent, piezoelectric, and exhibits a linear electrooptical effect. Its nonlinear tensor coefficients, applicable to Eq. (189), were given in Section 4.4.2; with them, we can write out three equations formally relating each component of the second-harmonic charge polarization to the three components of the fundamental optical field:

$$P_x^{(2\omega)} = d_{14} E_y^{(\omega)} E_z^{(\omega)}, \tag{208}$$

$$P_y^{(2\omega)} = d_{14} E_x^{(\omega)} E_z^{(\omega)}, \tag{209}$$

$$P_z^{(2\omega)} = d_{36} E_x^{(\omega)} E_y^{(\omega)}. \tag{210}$$

The respective field components depend on the intensity, direction of propagation, and sense of polarization of the fundamental wave.

Suppose it to be purely $O$-wave. Then there is no $Z$ component of $\mathbf{E}^{(\omega)}$, and therefore only one nonvanishing component of the charge polarization, directed along the $Z$ axis. Thus, ordinary-wave fundamental generates extraordinary-wave harmonic.

We have here the basis for index matching. Figure 22 shows the re-

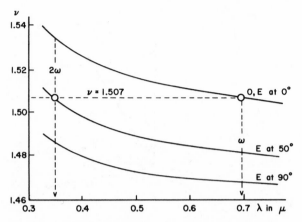

Figure 22. Index of refraction of potassium di-hydrogen phosphate ("KDP") as a function of wavelength for $O$ and $E$ polarizations and three different directions of propagation, showing that extraordinary harmonic waves propagating at $50°$ to the optic axis are phase-matched to the ordinary fundamental wave of a ruby laser.

fractive index of KDP for $O$-polarized light, together with that for $E$-polarized light beams propagating, respectively, at $0°$, $50°$, and $90°$ to the optic axis. Suppose we direct plane-polarized fundamental ruby-laser light [$\lambda = 6.943(-7)$ m] onto the crystal, cut and oriented in such manner that, after refraction (Section 4.7), this radiation in the crystal is $O$-polarized and propagating at an angle $\theta$ to the optic axis. Then the second harmonic will be $E$-polarized, and its index of refraction will be 1.507, just that of the exciting fundamental when $\theta \doteq 50°$.

*Birefringence must exceed dispersion* for matching to be possible. This is not generally true; quartz, for example, has insufficient birefringence to permit index matching in this way.* This requirement is clarified by Figure 23, which presents the refractive index information in another form, as a function of direction. The two parallel horizontal lines labeled $\nu_0(\omega)$ and $\nu_0(2\omega)$ are applicable values of the ordinary refractive index, which is independent of direction but not of frequency. The curve labeled $\nu_E(2\omega)$ is the extraordinary refractive index at the harmonic frequency, decreasing from identity with the ordinary index to its tabulated minimum value at

---

* It is still possible to generate appreciable second harmonic in quartz by means of a stack of thin plates with their optic axes alternating in direction by $180°$ and inclined so that their thicknesses are odd multiples of the coherence length.

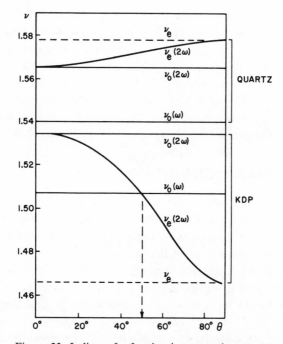

Figure 23. Indices of refraction in quartz (upper curves) and KDP for ruby-laser light and its second harmonic as functions of the direction of propagation.
In KDP, intersection of the curves for ordinary fundamental and extraordinary harmonic allows index
matching; in quartz, no intersection occurs and index
matching is impossible.

$\theta = 90°$. The point of intersection at $\theta = 50°$ determines the direction of
propagation at which index matching is possible in this particular crystal.
In quartz, the curve of $\nu_E(2\omega)$ does not cross the line $\nu_0(\omega)$.

With purely $E$-polarized fundamental, the electric vector has components along all three coordinate axes, except when $\theta = 90°$; in that extreme
case, no harmonic is present. Some second harmonic is generated with
$E$-polarization, but it cannot be phase matched with the $E$-polarized fundamental.

Alert readers may have wondered why the $X$ and $Y$ directions were
chosen at $45°$ to that direction which might seem a more natural choice
for either; namely, that of the electric vector of an ordinary wave. Moreover,
the value of the product $E_x^{(\omega)} E_y^{(\omega)}$ depends on this choice of $X$ direction
(and through it, of $Y$ direction). The value of $P_z^{(2\omega)}$ which the fundamental

wave excites is a property of the crystal, and, as such, it cannot depend on the particular coordinate system with which we choose to describe the phenomenon. It follows that the numerical values of the tensor coefficients are not independent of the coordinate system, but must obey a transformation law which preserves the constancy of $\mathbf{P}^{(2\omega)}$ as the coordinate system is rotated about the $Z$ axis. The particular choice made above is that for which the tabulated tensor coefficients apply. It can be shown that the principal axes of the index ellipsoid applicable to the Pockels effect are just these axes.

## 4.7. BOUNDARY CONDITIONS

Practical considerations dictate that coherent fundamental radiation be produced in a laser and introduced into the nonlinear medium from outside; it therefore must cross an optical discontinuity (unless, of course, the nonlinear medium is that of the laser).

In Section 2.2.3, general boundary conditions of electromagnetic theory were applied to derive laws of reflection and refraction. The same boundary conditions apply to nonlinear media, but the resulting phenomena are far more complicated, especially when birefringence is involved.

As an example, consider a beam of intense monochromatic light incident at angle $\theta_I$ on a plane face of a crystal of KDP. Imagine further that the crystal has been rotated about the normal to the incident face until its optic axis lies in the plane of incidence. Let the incident light be plane-polarized, either in $(E)$ or normal $(O)$ to the plane of incidence. In either case, only a single transmitted fundamental beam will exist within the crystal, directed at an angle $\theta_T$ with the normal. The angle $\theta_T$ and the corresponding propagation constant $k_T$ are found with the aid of Snell's law, using the appropriate $O$ or $E$ index of refraction evaluated at the fundamental frequency. A reflected ray at $\theta_R = \theta_I$ will of course be present as well (see Figure 24). Coordinate axes normal to the optic axis and oriented at $45°$ to the plane of incidence are also required for evaluating the harmonic radiation, as in the preceding section.

The transmitted fundamental beam excites an array of harmonic sources within the crystal as before, but these can radiate into the space above the crystal as well as in the generally forward sense.

For definiteness, let the incident radiation have ordinary polarization, a choice consistent with the result of the preceding section. The refracted beam will then also be $O$-polarized, its E-vector being directed normal to the optic axis, and thus have only $X$ and $Y$ components. It therefore excites a pure $Z$ component in the charge polarization, so as to radiate

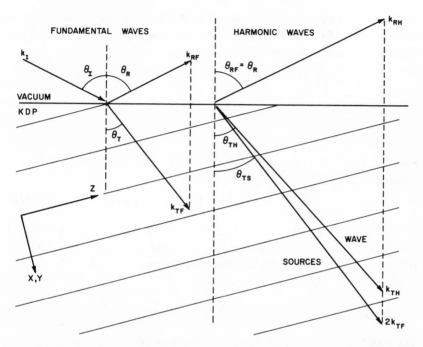

Figure 24. Propagation vectors of an incident fundamental wave and of the reflected and transmitted fundamental and harmonic waves it excites in a nonlinear medium.

$E$-polarized harmonic waves within the crystal and into the space above.

Returning to Figure 24, we see, displaced for clarity, the propagation vectors of the second harmonic waves for the special case treated. The nonlinear charge polarization (source distribution) is a wave of frequency $2\omega$ and propagation vector $2\mathbf{k}_{TF}$; it is therefore drawn parallel to the fundamental transmitted propagation vector $\mathbf{k}_{TF}$ and is of twice its length.

On the vacuum side, the source distribution radiates into the same direction as the reflected fundamental (vector $\mathbf{k}_{RH}$). In this uniaxial medium, there are, in the general case, two possible directions of propagation for the refracted fundamental radiation; in the special case considered, there is only one, and one corresponding component of nonlinear charge polarization, parallel to the optic axis; this can give rise only to a single free harmonic wave. The propagation vector for this wave is designated $\mathbf{k}_{TH}$; the corresponding index of refraction, which determines its magnitude, is that of extraordinary ($E$-wave) polarization at frequency $2\omega$ for a direction of propagation as yet undetermined.

Continuity of tangential components of $\mathbf{E}$ is required for each frequency as a boundary condition which holds for every instant of time. Applied at the fundamental frequency, this condition leads to Snell's law. The second harmonic waves are of the form

Nonlinear source:       $\exp i\{2\omega t - 2\mathbf{k}_{TF} \cdot \mathbf{r}\}$,

Free transmitted:       $\exp i\{2\omega t - \mathbf{k}_{TH} \cdot \mathbf{r}\}$,

Reflected:              $\exp i\{2\omega t - 2\mathbf{k}_{RF} \cdot \mathbf{r}\}$,

and, for $\mathbf{E}$ to be single-valued at all points along the boundary at every instant,

$$(2\mathbf{k}_{TF})_p = (\mathbf{k}_{TH})_p = (2\mathbf{k}_{RF})_p = (\mathbf{k}_{RH})_p, \tag{211}$$

where $(\cdots)_p$ denotes that component of each propagation vector which is parallel to the interface. Replacing these by equivalent expressions involving refractive indices and canceling common factors gives the equivalent of Snell's law for the harmonic waves,

$$\nu_0(\omega) \sin \theta_T = \nu_E(2\omega, \theta_{TH}) \sin \theta_{TH} = \sin \theta_{RF} = \sin \theta_{RH}. \tag{212}$$

The index $\nu_0$ is that for ordinary waves evaluated at the fundamental frequency; it has no directional dependence. The index $\nu_E$ applying to the harmonic is a function of direction. Graphical rather than analytic solution is required.

Examination of Eq. (212) reveals that if one varies $\theta_I$ until at a corresponding value of $\theta_{TH}$ the extraordinary refractive index at harmonic frequency is numerically equal to the ordinary fundamental index, the two transmitted beams become collinear as well as phase-matched. Otherwise, they will not propagate in the same direction, and they will beat in and out of phase. In KDP, the value of $\theta_{TH}$ must correspond to a 50° angle with the optic axis (not with the normal to the incident face).

In general, one must remember that $\mathbf{k}$, the wave vector, and $\mathbf{S}$, the energy flow vector, are not strictly collinear in birefringent media. When a narrow pencil of light is incident on a nonlinear medium, giving rise to refracted pencils of fundamental, source, and free-harmonic waves, the harmonic pencil does not remain with the fundamental pencil, even though indices are matched. Thus the second harmonic which emerges from the far face of a long medium is spread out over a line lying in the plane of $\mathbf{k}_{TH}$ and $\mathbf{S}_{TH}$.

The opposite choice of incident wave polarization ($E$) involves a more complicated problem because there will then be three generally unequal components of the resultant charge polarization. The second-harmonic radiation will therefore have both $O$- and $E$-wave polarizations propagating at unequal velocities and, therefore, not collinear. Neither can be index matched to the fundamental, however, so there is no practical need to examine this case in detail.

Intermediate planes of incident wave polarization of course establish two orthogonally polarized fundamental refracted waves, each propagating in its particular direction and generating a second-harmonic source distribution of distinct spatial period. Again, only the ordinary wave can be index matched to the harmonic.

Further application of boundary conditions to the other electromagnetic field vectors leads to relations among the amplitudes of the various waves analogous to Fresnel's equations. The method by which this is done has been presented in Section 2.2.3. For the actual formulas, the reader is referred to the original literature because of the many special situations and the algebraic complexity involved.

## 4.8. A NUMERICAL EXAMPLE

The possibility of matching phases of harmonic and fundamental having been established, one next inquires what beam power, conversion crystal dimensions, and degree of crystal perfection are required if SHG is to be useful in converting light at a longer wavelength to its harmonic.

The intensity of the second harmonic attains half its ultimate theoretical value when the harmonic field amplitude $E^{(2\omega)}$ reaches $1/\sqrt{2}$ of the initial fundamental amplitude $A$. From Eq. (185), the crystal thickness required for this degree of conversion is

$$z_{1/2} = (1/CA)\,\tanh^{-1}(1/\sqrt{2}) = 0.88/CA. \qquad (213)$$

Suppose the beam power to be $100\ \mathrm{MW/cm^2}$. The fundamental amplitude *in the crystal* can then be calculated from either Eq. (57) or (182). Using values applicable to KDP and a ruby laser, $\lambda = 6.943(-7)$ m, $\nu = 1.507$, and $S = 1.0(12)\ \mathrm{W/m^2}$.

The initial amplitude at the fundamental wavelength is

$$A = \left(\frac{2S}{\varepsilon_0 \nu c}\right)^{1/2} = \left(\frac{2.0(12)}{8.85(-12) \times 1.507 \times 3(8)}\right)^{1/2}$$
$$= 2.24(7)\quad \mathrm{V/m}.$$

This assumes, of course, that the laser beam is plane-polarized at the proper orientation, and it neglects reflection losses involved in concentrating and introducing the beam into the crystal.

Equation (206) also requires the nonlinear susceptibility coefficient $\chi_{NL}$. For index-matched KDP, the value

$$\chi_{NL} = 1.2(8) \quad \text{esu} = 3.18(-12) \quad \text{m/V}$$

has been reported. The conversion coefficient is then

$$C = \frac{\pi \times 3.18(-12)}{1.507 \times 6.943(-7)}$$

$$= 0.954(-5) \quad \text{V}^{-1}.$$

With this coefficient, a thickness of

$$Z_{1/2} = \frac{0.88}{0.954(-5) \times 2.24(7)} \quad \text{m}$$

$$= 4.11 \quad \text{mm}$$

will convert half of the fundamental beam power into the second harmonic, provided that the refractive indices are sufficiently well-matched to ensure a still greater coherence length; i.e.,

$$|\, v_2 - v_1 \,| < \lambda/4Z_{1/2} = 4(-6).$$

Note from Figure 23 that the index $v_e$ changes by approximately $(1.535 - 1.485) \div 90$, or $5.5(-4)$ for each angular degree by which the direction of propagation is changed from the correct $50°$ inclination. The crystal orientation must therefore be extremely precise, a feat which seems particularly difficult in view of the use of converging lenses with laser beams to achieve high local beam intensity. In the next section, we shall account for the success of convergent-beam SHG.

## 4.9. INDEX MATCHING AS MOMENTUM CONSERVATION

Since the wave vector $\mathbf{k}$ is the measure of photon momentum in units of $\hbar$, the refraction relations of Section 4.7 can be considered to express the constancy of the component of photon momentum parallel to the optical boundary. The forces between the various waves present and the medium are exerted normal to the interface.

Similarly, the index-matching requirement for the transmitted waves,

$$\mathbf{k}_{TH} = 2\mathbf{k}_{TF},\tag{214}$$

expresses the conservation of photon momentum; the momentum of each newly created single second-harmonic photon is the sum of the momenta of the two fundamental photons which coalesce to create it.

Viewed from this standpoint, the condition becomes less restrictive. With a slight change of notation, the above can be generalized to

$$\mathbf{k}^{(2\omega)} = \mathbf{k}^{(\omega)} + \mathbf{k}^{(\omega')},\tag{215}$$

in which $\mathbf{k}^{(\omega)}$ and $\mathbf{k}^{(\omega')}$ are the momenta of two fundamental photons, each of frequency $\omega$, which now need not necessarily be collinear, so long as the vector relationship is satisfied exactly. A spread of photon directions therefore exists which can be matched, allowing the use of convergent beams from focused lasers for SHG.

## 4.10. HARMONICS HIGHER THAN THE SECOND

The treatment of SHG given above can be extended to third harmonic with little change in the conceptual framework, but with considerable change in detail. The third-order nonlinear susceptibility tensor must be used to find the nonlinear source terms analogous to those of Eqs. (194) and (195),

$$P_i^{(3\omega)} = \varepsilon_0 \chi_{ijkl}^{(3\omega)} E_j^{(\omega)} E_k^{(\omega)} E_l^{(\omega)}\tag{216}$$

$$P_i^{(\omega)} = \varepsilon_0 \chi_{ijkl}^{(\omega)} E_j^{(3\omega)} E_k^{(\omega)} E_l^{(\omega)},\tag{217}$$

and to relate the polarizations of incident and harmonic waves. Index matching is more difficult because of the greater dispersion.

Harmonics higher than third are practically unobservable because sufficient birefringence does not exist to meet the index-matching requirement. Generation of fourth-harmonic has been claimed; it actually consisted of two successive steps of SHG using a pair of crystals at the slightly different matching angles for $(\omega \to 2\omega)$ and $(2\omega \to 4\omega)$.

In calcite, using ruby-laser radiation, third harmonic can be matched to the fundamental at $57°$ to the optical axis, with wave polarizations such that two ordinary and one extraordinary photons interact to produce one extraordinary photon of triple frequency. The third harmonic, $\lambda = 2448$ Å, is in the middle ultraviolet. The conversion efficiency is very low.

## 4.11. OPTICAL RECTIFICATION

It is well known that second-order nonlinearity evokes a net average displacement as well as a double-frequency response to an applied periodic driving force. The magnitude of the static term is proportional to the square of the amplitude of the driving force, Eq. (171).

We therefore expect the electrical response of an optical medium with second-order nonlinearity to include a constant charge polarization as well as a second harmonic. This is the optical-frequency analog of "detection" by rectification, which is of great practical importance at radio frequency.

Thus a dielectric slab through which intense polarized light is passing will be electrically polarized; it is as though a static electric field were also applied to it by a pair of capacitor plates. Such an electrode pair placed on opposite sides of the slab can transmit an induced voltage signal to a detector, indicating the passage of the light; the signal amplitude should be proportional to the laser beam intensity and a maximum in the direction of wave polarization.

Obviously, considerations of phasing, coherence length, or index matching do not apply to this phenomenon. Dispersion still complicates the problem, however; the tensor components which relate the dc charge polarization to the impressed wave are *not* identical with those for harmonic generation. They are, in fact, more closely related to those of the linear electrooptical effect.

To describe the dc effect quantitatively, Eq. (189), the expression for the $i$th component of the second-order polarization at double frequency, must be supplemented by a second term

$$P_i^{(0)} = \varepsilon_0 \chi_{ijk}^{(0)} E_j^{(\omega)} E_k^{(\omega)}, \tag{218}$$

which describes the dc component of the nonlinear polarization. The two tensor coefficients differ; i.e., $\chi_{ijk}^{(0)} \neq \chi_{ijk}^{(2\omega)}$ because of dispersion.

Equation (218) is closely related to Eq. (156) for the linear electrooptical (Pockels) effect, in which a dc electric field modifies the susceptibility for optical-frequency fields. In the present notation Eq. (156) becomes

$$P_i^{(\omega)} = \varepsilon_0 \chi_{ijk}^{(\omega)} E_j^{(0)} E_k^{(\omega)}. \tag{219}$$

In this expression, two field components, one at optical and the other at zero frequency, must be multiplied; the susceptibility is evaluated at optical frequency.

It is a remarkable fact that the tensor coefficients applicable to optical rectification can be determined directly by measurements of the Pockels effect using dc electric fields and light of the harmonic frequency. The basis for this fact is that quantum-mechanical formulas for these coefficients show that

$$\chi_{ijk}^{(0)} = \chi_{jik}^{(\omega)}. \tag{220}$$

Equations (218) and (219) differ only by the interchange of field frequency and component index between the susceptibility and one of the electric field factors.

These considerations are important in the low-frequency modulation and demodulation of optical beams by means of Pockels cells.

Special care is needed in observing the dc effect because of pyroelectric effects and the necessarily extremely short duration of the intense light required to produce it. Although the voltage generated is not dependent on the mode pattern of the laser, whenever several slightly different frequencies are present, their rectification gives a "low" beat frequency as well as a "dc" signal. This beat can be at radio frequency. The dc effect occurs even if a strong absorption band at $2\omega$ prevents appreciable generation of second harmonic or even if the fundamental is close to a strong absorption band.

Measurements confirm the theoretical identity of the Pockels and rectification coefficients, the quadratic dependence on intensity of the inducing light, and the $\sin^2 \theta$ dependence on the wave polarization.

An analogous effect occurs with circularly polarized light. Just as plane-polarized beams create an electric field, the passage of a circularly polarized beam generates a magnetic field — the inverse Faraday effect.

## 4.12. OPTICAL MIXING AND PARAMETRIC AMPLIFICATION

Optical second-harmonic generation and rectification are the special case of mixing of two intense primary light beams in a passive nonlinear medium, in which the two beams have the *same* frequency. A less restricted situation, and one of considerable practical interest, is that in which two or more primary beams *not* of the same frequency interact with a nonlinear dielectric. One then observes combination frequencies (sum and difference in the two-beam case) in addition to the harmonic and dc components, originating in nonlinear response to the beats between the primary frequency components. Analogous "intermodulation" phenomena are known in acoustics and electronics. The optical wave-mixing phenomena are far more complicated because the susceptibility coefficients which account for them are frequency-dependent tensor elements, sensitive to directions of the various field and propagation vectors with respect to crystal axes.

The constitutive relations applicable to two-wave frequency mixing are

$$P_i^{(\omega_2-\omega_1)} = \varepsilon_0 \chi_{ijk}^{(\omega_2-\omega_1)} E_j^{(\omega_2)} E_k^{(\omega_1)'}, \tag{221}$$

applying to difference-frequency generation, and

$$P_i^{(\omega_2+\omega_1)} = \varepsilon_0 \chi_{ijk}^{(\omega_2+\omega_1)} E_j^{(\omega_2)} E_k^{(\omega_1)}, \tag{222}$$

applying to the sum. Similar, more involved relations exist in the case of three-wave and higher-order mixing processes. The relations for harmonic generation also apply, so that the complete expression for the charge polarization consists of at least six terms, two at the primary frequencies, two for harmonic and dc response, and the two written here. These provide the source terms of wave equations, one for each component. The waves which are mixed and the combination waves they produce need not be collinear. The direction of propagation of each of the various waves will be determined by the spatial distribution of the respective nonlinear sources and by the applicable index of refraction; dispersion plays the same role as in harmonic generation, usually preventing growth of any of the combination waves unless, by exploiting birefringence, one can achieve an index match. In a few cases, this proves possible for one mixture component; it can then be amplified. The others, not being index matched, can be neglected in calculating the growth of the favored component.

In the quantum theory, optical mixing is the coalescence of photons. In second-harmonic generation, pairs of identical photons coalesce; in sum-frequency generation, two photons of energy $\hbar\omega_1$ and $\hbar\omega_2$, respectively, combine to produce a single photon of energy $\hbar(\omega_2 + \omega_1)$. Since the medium cannot, on the average, transfer either energy or momentum to the combination wave, momentum as well as energy must be conserved in the interaction. Recalling the significance of $\mathbf{k}$ as a measure of photon momentum, we must write

$$\mathbf{k}^{(\omega_2)} + \mathbf{k}^{(\omega_1)} = \mathbf{k}^{(\omega_2+\omega_1)} \tag{223}$$

in the sum-generation case and

$$\mathbf{k}^{(\omega_2)} + \mathbf{k}^{(\omega_1)} = \mathbf{k}^{(\omega_2-\omega_1)} \tag{224}$$

for the difference-frequency process, expressing the requirement of conservation of momentum, one of which must hold if its respective wave is to grow. Otherwise, the mismatch

$$\Delta \mathbf{k} = \mathbf{k}^{(\omega_2 + \omega_1)} - (\mathbf{k}^{(\omega_2)} + \mathbf{k}^{(\omega_1)}) \tag{225}$$

introduces a phase factor $\exp i\{\Delta \mathbf{k} \cdot \mathbf{r}\}$, which alternates in sign as the combination wave progresses. Referring to Eq. (177), one recognizes $\Delta k$ as the reciprocal of the coherence length (with a factor of $1/\pi$).

We shall now calculate the growth of a sum-frequency wave in a nonlinear medium through which two primary waves of frequency $\omega_2$ and $\omega_1$ are passed. The sum wave, of frequency

$$\omega_3 = \omega_2 + \omega_1, \tag{226}$$

is assumed to be index matched according to Eq. (223). Since the beams are assumed collinear, the two primary $k$'s are additive, and the indices of refraction therefore satisfy the condition

$$v_3 \omega_3 = v_2 \omega_2 + v_1 \omega_1. \tag{227}$$

One way in which this condition may be met is for all three refractive indices to be equal. More generally, some way must be found to exploit birefringence, as explained in Section 4.6. Let us simplify the present discussion by assuming that a common refractive index $v$ has been achieved in some manner, ignoring the details of wave polarization. We also ignore the problems of introducing the beams into the mixing crystal.

The problem is therefore reduced to that of setting up and solving coupled propagation equations for the amplitudes of three interacting waves, given their initial amplitudes and phase relationships. This resembles the problem of Section 4.5, except that three distinct frequencies now are present, and the coupling terms are those of Eqs. (221) and (222). Note that either fundamental can interact with the sum frequency to generate the other as a difference frequency.

The phases of the component waves are as yet unspecified; they are written in exponential notation with complex amplitude. By choice of time-zero, we can make the amplitude of the sum wave purely real. Thus each of the respective electric waves is of the form

$$E_i^{\{\omega i} = \tfrac{1}{2} A_i \exp i\{\omega_i[t - (vz/c)]\} + \tfrac{1}{2} \bar{A}_i \exp -i\{\omega_i[t - (vz/c)]\}, \tag{228}$$

where the index $i$ is 1 or 2 for fundamentals and 3 for the sum, and in the case of the latter, the amplitude $A_3$ is equal to its conjugate $\bar{A}_3$.

Combining in pairs, we obtain coupling factors analogous to Eqs. (198) and (199). The sum-wave propagation equation contains a source term, derived with Eq. (122), in which there is a factor

$$(E_1 E_2)^{(\omega_3)} = \tfrac{1}{4} A_1 A_2 \exp i\{\omega_3[t - (vz/c)]\} + \tfrac{1}{4} \bar{A}_1 \bar{A}_2 \exp -i\{\omega_3[t - (vz/c)]\}. \tag{229}$$

This accounts for all those terms in the product $E_1 E_2$ which vary at *sum* frequency. Two other terms, varying at the *difference* frequency $\omega_1 - \omega_2$, are of no concern in the present discussion because they are, by assumption, not index matched.

Coupling of $\omega_3$ and $\omega_1$ waves involves the product

$$(E_3 E_1)^{(\omega_2)} = \tfrac{1}{4} A_3 \bar{A}_1 \exp i\{\omega_2[t - (vz/c)]\} + \tfrac{1}{4} A_3 A_1 \exp -i\{\omega_2[t - (vz/c)]\} \tag{230}$$

and the sum and $\omega_2$ waves similarly involve the product

$$(E_3 E_2)^{(\omega_1)} = \tfrac{1}{4} A_3 \bar{A}_2 \exp i\{\omega_1[t - (vz/c)]\} + \tfrac{1}{4} A_3 A_2 \exp -i\{\omega_1[t - (vz/c)]\} \tag{231}$$

as a factor in Eq. (221). The complex amplitudes are needed to regulate the phasing of the respective waves.

Propagation equations, two analogous to Eq. (194) and one, for the sum wave, analogous to Eq. (195), can now be written and approximated by first-order equations for the amplitude growth using reasoning similar to that following Eq. (201). The resulting set of three coupled equations for the complex field amplitudes can be written in several ways. The forms

$$dA_3/dz = -i\omega_3 \chi^{(\omega_1 + \omega_2)} A_1 A_2/2vc, \tag{232}$$

$$d\bar{A}_2/dz = +i\omega_2 \chi^{(\omega_3 - \omega_1)} A_3 A_1/2vc, \tag{233}$$

$$dA_1/dz = -i\omega_1 \chi^{(\omega_3 - \omega_2)} A_3 \bar{A}_2/2vc, \tag{234}$$

are closely analogous to Eqs. (204) and (205). As with those equations, constancy of total energy flow is implicit in these equations, *provided* the three susceptibility factors are equal, a condition which holds only as a good approximation; it also implies the complete absence of absorption, an impossibility for dispersive media.

Assuming equality of the susceptibility factors, we can lump the properties of the nonlinear medium into a single factor $\chi_{NL}/2vc$ of dimensions second/volt.

Making the substitution

$$Q_i = A_i/\sqrt{\omega_i} \tag{235}$$

and defining the quantity

$$K = A_3 \chi_{\mathrm{NL}} \sqrt{\omega_1 \omega_2}/2\nu c, \tag{236}$$

recasts the amplitude equations into the forms, symmetrical in $Q_1$ and $\bar{Q}_2$,

$$dQ_3/dz = -iK^2 Q_1 Q_2/Q_3, \tag{237}$$

$$d\bar{Q}_2/dz = +iKQ_1, \tag{238}$$

$$dQ_1/dz = -iK\bar{Q}_2. \tag{239}$$

This form of the coupled amplitude-growth equations is useful because the squares of the amplitudes of the $Q$-variables are measures of the respective flux densities of photons in each component. It can readily be shown that they state a conservation law: for every photon created at energy $\hbar\omega_3$, a photon is removed at each of the other frequencies (and conversely).

Multiplying through by $c/\nu$ converts each equation for amplitude growth of a traveling wave with distance into an equation for the growth of amplitude of a standing wave with time; the resulting equations are applicable to optical mixing in a Fabry–Perot resonator. Here one must take note of absorption; otherwise, physically unrealistic performance would be predicted. To do this, one adds to each right-hand side a loss term $-Q_i/\tau_i$ proportional to the respective field variable; with this added term, in the absence of the other two waves, each field amplitude decays exponentially with time constant $\tau_i$. One then finds that there are threshold amplitudes above which the optical mixing terms will dominate, their positive contribution to the time derivative of $Q_3$ then exceeding the negative contribution due to absorption.

Since both sum- and difference-frequency generation are taking place, the above approach to outlining the theory of optical mixing is completely general. This theory applies whenever three waves interact in a nonlinear medium, provided their frequencies are related by Eq. (226) and that the index-matching requirement is met. Various possibilities are contained in the choice of initial conditions.

One particularly important case of three-wave coupling is that in which a strong wave at $\omega_3$, called the "pump," interacts with a weak wave at $\omega_1$, called the "signal," in a nonlinear crystal, to amplify the signal wave. In this optical analog of the parametric amplifier, a second wave at

$\omega_2$, called "idler" wave, is simultaneously generated; the interaction converts pump photons of energy $\hbar\omega_3$ into pairs of one signal and one idler photon. The initial condition for this process is that $Q_3$ is very large, so that, from Eqs. (237)–(239), its derivative is small, although those of the other two waves can be large. We can then consider $Q_3$ a constant factor and find approximate solutions to Eqs. (238) and (239). Note further that even if $\bar{Q}_2$ is initially zero, interaction of the signal and pump ensures idler-wave growth, so that $\bar{Q}_2$ at once begins to contribute to the growth of the signal $\bar{Q}_1$. The solutions closely resemble that of the traveling-wave SHG problem:

$$Q_1 = Q_0 \cosh Kz, \tag{240}$$

$$\bar{Q}_2 = iQ_0 \sinh Kz, \tag{241}$$

where $Q_0$ is the initial value of the signal-wave variable at $z = 0$.

In practice, this process has been carried out by first converting a neodymium-laser beam to its second harmonic in KDP or in lithium niobate, so as to furnish a pump at $\lambda = 0.53\mu$. The second-harmonic beam is then introduced into a second nonlinear crystal; either the crystal orientation or the temperature is varied to "tune" the system to the signal frequency so as to satisfy the three-wave index-matching condition.

Another use for the three-wave process is to convert very-long-wavelength coherent radiation to a more easily detected shorter wavelength.

Optical mixing may also occur inadvertently when the active atoms of a laser medium contain nearly equal quantities of two or more isotopes. In ferroelectric media, the index-matching condition is not stringent, and two slightly different frequencies generate their respective harmonics, $2\omega_1$ and $2\omega_2$, together with the mixture $\omega_1 + \omega_2$, all of which vanish when the temperature is raised above the Curie point.

Formally similar considerations apply to the interaction of three primary beams to produce a combination frequency. Obviously, the difficulty of index matching makes this problem of academic interest only.

## 4.13. SELF-FOCUSING OF OPTICAL BEAMS

Optical mixing, rectification, and harmonic generation are for all practical purposes confined to crystalline solids, not only because they are closely related to the Pockels, or linear electrooptical effect, but also because the index-matching problem demands birefringence. Conceivably, one could match indices by exploiting the difference in phase velocity of right- and left-circular polarization in optically active solutions of noncentrosymmetrical molecules; in practice, the amount of optical rotation available is insufficient to overcome dispersion. Moreover, in liquids, other phenomena are observed which would make it practically hopeless to accomplish a stable matching of refractive indices, and which, moreover, tend to destroy the geometry of an intense light beam.

It was noted in Section 3.8 that many liquids exhibit a quadratic electro-optical effect, their indices of refraction varying as the square of the electric field intensity regardless of the directions of propagation or wave polarization. This, the Kerr effect, involves alignment of large, nonspherical molecules by electric fields. Although such molecules cannot change their alignment at optical frequency, and so do not *follow* the electric field variation, nevertheless, they do acquire an appreciable *orientation* after relatively very short times of exposure to intense optical fields, and, thereafter, the liquid has an effective susceptibility which is appreciably different from that in its normal state of thermally maintained randomness in molecular orientation.

Even in liquids which do not show the Kerr effect, in gases and in amorphous quasiliquid solids like glass, some intensity dependence of the refractive index exists because of electrostriction. This was shown in Section 3.7 to change the density to an extent proportional to the square of the electric field intensity. Just as intense light generates dc electric polarization in media with second-order nonlinearity, it will create a net increase in density, and therefore of refractive index, in any isotropic dielectric, whether linear or not.

It is interesting to consider possible consequences of a dependence of the refractive index of an amorphous solid or liquid on the intensity of a light beam, i.e., on the square of the optical electric field intensity. Symbolically,

$$\nu = \nu_0 + JE^2. \tag{242}$$

At once, a variation of optical thickness with light intensity suggests itself. But there are much more startling consequences, which have caused a great deal of trouble in nonlinear optical research.

The finite lateral extent of actual light beams has not been of importance to the discussions of previous sections, except where we have noted the use of convergent beams from lenses in SHG. This is permissible where the linear electrooptical effect, the dominant phenomenon, is important at moderately high light intensities. Since no beam can be unlimited in transverse extent, at higher intensities the more intense central core of the beam refracts to a different extent than its less intense peripheral regions.

Most optical setups are intended to produce and employ light beams having cylindrical symmetry (although the actual mode pattern of a laser system may depart significantly from this, having both azimuthal and radial structure), the intensity decreasing continuously from the center to the outside. In the vicinity of the focal point of a concentrating lens system, for example, the combined effect of source and lens characteristics, and of diffraction is to establish a bell-shaped radial intensity variation similar to the normal error, or Gaussian, function. Such radial decrease of intensity establishes a radial dependence of optical thickness, i.e., a *lens in the medium.* Even when the light beam is concentrated outside and introduced into the medium as a parallel pencil of rays, this automatic focusing effect tends to curve its plane wavefronts, causing the pencil to contract further, increasing the local intensity and thereby further aggravating the effect. The result is analogous to the "pinch effect" observed in an intense electron beam in which space charge but not the self-magnetic field has been partially neutralized by slower ions which the beam creates in the residual gas.

A limit to the self-contraction is reached under appropriate conditions, the beam forming a filamentary guide within the medium within which it remains trapped by total internal reflection, as though in an optical fiber.

An elementary argument establishes the possibility if not the stability of such a virtual fiber in any medium having a positive value of $J$ in Eq. (242). Suppose the radiation to be confined within a filament of circular cross section with diameter $d$, across which its intensity is essentially uniform. The confined light of wavelength $\lambda$ is diffracted by a circular opening of this diameter; the first minimum of the diffraction pattern is at an angle

$$\theta = 1.22\lambda/\nu d \qquad (243)$$

to the beam axis. This relation, of course, must not predict absurdly large values for $\theta$; otherwise, beam propagation could never take place within the fiber. The angle $\theta$ must therefore be small, and $d$ therefore large in comparison with $\lambda$. If $\theta$ is less than the critical angle $\theta_c$ for total internal reflection at the surface of the fiber, most of the diffracted light is trapped, unable to emerge into the lower-index medium outside.

Thus the self-trapping condition is

$$\theta < \theta_c, \qquad (244)$$

where the critical angle is found by applying Snell's law

$$\theta_c = \cos^{-1}[\nu_0/(\nu_0 + JE^2)]$$
$$\doteq \cos^{-1}[1 - (JE^2/\nu_0)]. \qquad (245)$$

The small-angle cosine approximation gives

$$\theta_c{}^2 = 2JE^2/\nu_0. \qquad (246)$$

A self-maintaining filament can therefore exist if

$$E^2/\lambda^2 > 0.744/J\nu_0 d^2. \qquad (247)$$

Suppose $J$ to be of the same order as the ordinary Kerr coefficient. In nitrobenzene, for example, $\nu_0 = 1.55$ and $J = 2.45(-15)$ m²/V²; at the light intensity assumed in the example of Section 4.8, the quantity $JE^2/\nu_0$ already exceeds unity, and the small-angle approximation is inapplicable. We can accordingly expect appreciable departure from "good" optical behavior even at intensities below $10^{12}$ W/m² in nitrobenzene and even though the Kerr coefficient applicable to optical fields is far lower than that for radio-frequency fields.

# 5.

## NONLINEAR OPTICAL PHENOMENA IN ACTIVE MEDIA

### 5.1. SIMILARITIES AND CONTRASTS

**5.1.1. Spontaneous and Stimulated Scattering.** Chapter 4 described phenomena in which photons are exchanged among two or more light beams having simply-related phases and frequencies. The harmonic, subharmonic, or mixture frequencies which are generated in those processes are determined only by the frequency composition of the applied light beam. Although indispensible to these processes, a nonlinear optical medium plays only a catalytic role, even when by its crystal symmetry and by fortuitous phase matching, it singles out one of several possible processes. As in ordinary linear dispersion, the medium responds coherently, but in a passive manner, to the electromagnetic disturbance. Photons collide elastically with the atomic systems; i.e., no detectable exchange of quanta occurs between the light waves and the dispersion systems, and the new frequencies generated are not characteristic of the medium. When sufficient care is taken to satisfy the rather stringent demands of coherence, a passive optical medium may act as an amplifier, facilitating the sustained exchange of energy between light beams. Such energy exchange, accomplished with coherently driven scattering systems, is more nearly akin to *stimulated* than to *spontaneous* emission.

Several additional classes of nonlinear optical phenomena exist, in which the optical medium is not merely a passive element, but imposes its own characteristic frequencies on that of the impressed light. These processes also involve coherent response to the electromagnetic disturbance, but in these cases, the internal structures of their optically responsive electronic systems are modified periodically by internal vibrations, typically mechanical. They accordingly present to the electromagnetic field a periodically varying susceptibility, and this modulates the light wave. Viewed quantum-mechanically, these processes involve *inelastic* collisions of photons with molecules or aggregates of molecules.

Chapter 3, devoted to the scattering of light by dispersion systems, included elementary discussions of Raman processes, as these are often collectively called. They comprise, besides the scattering of light by certain molecules with internal vibrational modes (which is the true Raman process), light scattering by acoustic waves (Brillouin scattering), by plasma oscillations, and by oriented electron-spin systems in certain types of solids. There the discussion centered on processes which, from the quantum-mechanical standpoint, are *spontaneous*.

The interest of nonlinear optics extends beyond the spontaneous phenomena. It also embraces *stimulated* scattering processes characterized not merely by the long-known feature of vibration-affected optical susceptibility, but by the recently discovered fact that *the optical electromagnetic field can excite and amplify the vibrations* if it exceeds a threshold intensity. The *light* wave then scatters the *sound* wave coherently.

Stimulated-scattering processes require intense, coherent beams from lasers for their full development. They then constitute the most spectacular of all optical phenomena. Stimulated Raman scattering is strikingly colorful; stimulated Brillouin processes are often manifested by perceptible sounds and even, in solids, by mechanical damage.

### 5.1.2. Raman and Brillouin Processes. In this chapter we shall treat Raman and Brillouin processes in more detail than other active-medium nonlinear interactions.

Brillouin and Raman scattering are fundamentally similar. Each occurs because a nonlinear property of an optical medium couples a mechanical variable (interatomic distance in a molecule, density in a homogeneous solid or liquid) to the charge polarization accompanying an electromagnetic wave. In each, the frequency spectrum of an electromagnetic wave is modified by an exchange of energy with the medium, in which phonons are emitted or absorbed.

The distinction of theoretical significance between these two processes is that Raman phenomena involve the (internal) vibrational states of molecules, while Brillouin scattering is associated with density variations of media which can be considered to have no other internal structure. Put in more sophisticated language, Raman processes involve the optical branches and Brillouin processes the acoustical branch, of the mechanical dispersion relation. The latter will be explained in a following section.

The practical distinctions are more significant. Raman processes produce light while Brillouin processes produce sound as well. Raman scattering generates new frequencies shifted by sharply defined magnitudes, comparable with optical frequencies; Brillouin scattering shifts the frequency while generating ultrasonic vibrations of frequencies depending on the direction of scattering.

There is another important difference in the characters of Raman and Brillouin interactions. In the former, since the mechanical disturbance is within individual molecules, usually of a liquid or gas — and these may not be appreciably coupled to their neighbors — the excitation does not propagate in the medium as a coherent wave, although it may be transferred to other molecules in collisions. Wave propagation necessitates interactions between molecules, even though they be no more than the random elastic molecular collisions which account for the propagation of sound in gases. The latter can propagate even in fluids as well-defined waves, but the internal excitations cannot.

This last distinction also suggests that as a rule, the frequency displacements in Raman scattering are apt to be much greater than those typical of Brillouin scattering. Raman-displaced spectral lines are easily distinguished with simple spectroscopic equipment; Brillouin-shifted lines require an interferometer to resolve them from the parent line.

### 5.1.3. Stokes and Anti-Stokes Frequency Shifts. In both Raman and Brillouin phenomena, the mixing of mechanical oscillations with a light beam in a nonlinear dielectric can create upshifts as well as downshifts in frequency. The latter, obedient to Stokes' law, are termed Stokes shifts; they occur because a phonon is emitted into the medium, and, its energy being provided at the expense of a photon in the primary light beam, a photon of lower energy must appear in the scattered light, which therefore is of lowered frequency. For an *anti*-Stokes, or *up*shift process, a phonon in the medium must coalesce with a primary photon to produce a new photon of higher energy (Section 3.11).

The conservation laws of energy and of momentum apply to both processes, of course. The close relationships of energy to frequency and of momentum to wave vector, central to the treatments in Chapter 4, are equally important in the interactions of light and mechanical waves. As we have seen, they relate the classical requirements of coherence among the several interacting wave fields to the conservation requirements for interactions among photons and phonons. The relation of $k$ to $\omega$ for each kind of wave we recall as its dispersion relation.

**5.1.4. Acoustic and Optical Dispersion.** It is instructive to contrast the general features of the dispersion relationships for light waves (Figure 25) with those for sound waves (Figures 26 and 27). Figure 25 is drawn for light in a hypothetical isotropic dielectric with a single natural frequency $\omega_0$ somewhere in the ultraviolet. The slope of this curve is the signal velocity of a group or packet of light waves with frequencies centered at the point of evaluation; the slope of a line from the origin to this point is the phase velocity, $c/v$, as required by Eq. (178). There is one curve, continuous except in the region of anomalous dispersion centered at $\omega_0$.

Figure 26 is drawn for sound in a hypothetical liquid containing diatomic molecules having one simple mode of internal mechanical vibration; e.g., oscillation at frequency $\omega_v$ along the line of centers of the molecule. There are two "branches," one for sound, or acoustic disturbances, and the other for the interatomic vibrations. The latter, being localized, non-propagating disturbances having vanishing group velocity, are represented by a horizontal line at height $\omega_v$. The significance of $k$ here is in representing the various phase relationships which might exist if the independent oscillations were excited in a coherent fashion. Ordinary sound waves, propagating at a velocity $v_s(\omega)$, and of much lower frequency range, are represented by

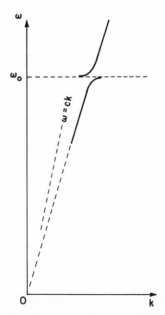

Figure 25. Dispersion relation for light in a transparent medium with a single natural frequency $\omega_0$.

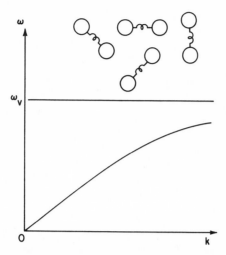

Figure 26. Dispersion relation for a hypothetical gas composed of diatomic molecules
with a single vibrational frequency and negligible rotational inertia, showing an acoustical
(lower) and an optical (upper) branch.

the lower curve, much more like the electromagnetic dispersion curve
except that $v_s \ll c$. Frequencies so high that the wavelength must approach
molecular dimensions are, of course, excluded from the acoustical branch,
which deals with pressure/density waves.

Figure 27 is drawn for a "one-dimensional solid" comprising an infinitely long chain of alternating light and heavy atoms, each coupled by an
elastic link or spring to its nearest neighbor. Because of the chainlike
coupling, interatomic vibrations can propagate; involving the least massive
elements, tightest binding forces, and shortest possible wavelength, they
can propagate with much higher phase velocity than the acoustic waves.
Their frequencies can be comparable with optical frequencies, and the
applicable dispersion relation is the upper curve, which asymptotically
approaches $\omega_2$ at small $k$, and $\omega_1$ at large $k$. The first of these limiting
frequencies corresponds to motion of the smaller masses with the larger
held fixed; the second, to the opposite extreme.

Extended to actual solids, which can support transverse as well as
longitudinal acoustic waves, or even to homogeneous liquids with complicated molecules, the mechanical dispersion relations become quite involved,
and we shall not attempt or need to consider them in more detail.

It is the lowest, or "acoustical" branch with which we are concerned

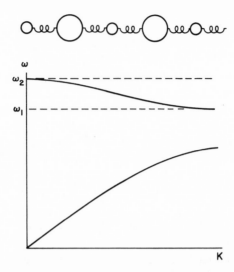

Figure 27. Dispersion relation for an infinitely
extended linear molecule composed of elastically coupled alternating unequal masses,
showing an acoustical (lower) branch and an
optical branch with two limiting frequencies.

in Brillouin scattering processes. Some of the higher, or "optical," branches
may be involved in Raman scattering.

**5.1.5. Coupling of Electromagnetic and Mechanical
Vibrations.** We must next inquire as to mechanisms by which purely
mechanical oscillations can be excited by electromagnetic radiation. These
mechanisms are quite different for the two kinds of scattering process.

In Brillouin scattering, the relevant quantities are macroscopic variables,
density and dielectric susceptibility. That the dielectric constant is a function
of the density is demonstrated by the Debye–Sears effect; electrostriction,
in turn, provides a mechanism by which the electronic polarization creates
pressure variations, and so allows light to pump a sound wave. The details
of this coupling will, of course, be different in solids than in fluids.

The Raman effect arises because the electronic polarizability is altered
when an interatomic distance within the molecule is changed; stimulated
Raman scattering arises because the interatomic binding forces are, in
turn, slightly altered when the electron cloud is displaced. Here one is
concerned with microscopic variables.

It is therefore reasonable to expect classical theory to suffice for the description of stimulated Brillouin scattering. On the other hand, in Raman scattering, quantum-mechanical considerations are important. Selection rules, for example, determine the vibrational transitions which are excited or stimulated. The Raman susceptibility is formally very similar to the second order nonlinear susceptibility of Chapter 4, and like it, must be calculated by quantum theory.

The stimulated Raman effect can be described quantitatively by equations almost identical to those used in Chapter 4 to account for the parametric interaction of two or more light waves. Stimulated Brillouin scattering, on the other hand, involves a sound wave interacting with two light waves, and the coupling terms in the respective wave equations are not alike.

## 5.2. RAMAN PROCESSES

### 5.2.1. Stimulated Raman Scattering. Although it was anticipated that laser beams would be especially useful in Raman spectroscopy, the discovery of *stimulated* Raman scattering was a surprise.

Raman scattering involves different selection rules than those applicable to emission and absorption processes. In particular, vibrational states which cannot combine directly with the ground state are accessible to Raman transitions. This has made Raman spectroscopy a valuable supplement to ordinary infrared and optical spectroscopy.

Because the anti-Stokes line appears in a normally-forbidden transition induced by incident light from an excited state to the ground state, the intensity of the incident light must be high, not only to maintain an adequate population in the excited state, but also to provide a sufficiently high flux of photons to induce the combination transition.

The ability of lasers to produce light of extremely high intensity makes them especially attractive sources for Raman spectroscopy of molecules by increasing the intensity of the anti-Stokes components in the Raman effect. Each resulting pair of lines, equally displaced with respect to the laser line, reveals a characteristic vibrational frequency of the molecule.

The need for high intensity in this and many other fields of optical research provided an incentive to the development of various techniques for the giant-pulsing of lasers. This in turn led to the unexpected discovery of Raman laser action. One of the earliest methods to accomplish this employed a repetitively-pulsed Kerr cell as an electrooptical shutter, or "$Q$-switch," enclosed within the laser "cavity," together with a polarizing prism (Figure 28). This allows laser action to occur only during the brief

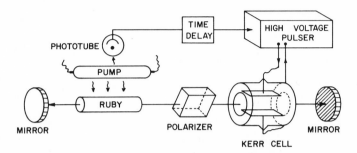

Figure 28. Setup for pulsed operation of a laser employing a Kerr cell as an electrooptical shutter. By delaying the opening of the Kerr cell, the ruby can be pumped to a higher state of excitation before stimulated emission discharges it. The Kerr cell also functions as a Raman cell.

time intervals when the Kerr cell is transmitting; the laser avalanche then discharges energy stored over the much longer time interval since the preceding pulse on the Kerr cell. It was noticed that for sufficiently high laser-pulse intensity, the 6943 Å ruby-laser line is accompanied by a satellite line at 7670 Å which originates in the nitrobenzene of the Kerr cell. The satellite line increases markedly in intensity as the laser output is increased above a threshold level of the order of 1 MW/cm², persists only while the laser output is above this threshold, shares the direction of the laser radiation, and becomes spectrally narrower at higher intensities. Its wavelength agrees with that of the known Raman–Stokes shift in nitrobenzene. The conclusion was therefore reached that the phenomenon is a *stimulated* Raman scattering process, pumped by the laser beam and resonated by the end-reflectors of the laser.

This interpretation has been sustained. Raman media are now widely used in conjunction with pulsed lasers to generate coherent radiation at frequencies other than those currently accessible to direct laser action. For this reason, the Raman scattering process has taken on a practical significance beyond its original one as a powerful spectroscopic technique.

**5.2.2. Theoretical Discussion.** The quantitative theory of stimulated Raman emission is complicated by several circumstances. The laser beam, at fundamental frequency $\omega$, first generates a Stokes-shifted beam and some anti-Stokes radiation; these also interact in the medium to generate Raman lines of higher order, which cannot be suppressed by index-mismatching. There can be gain for Stokes waves in any direction. Moreover, beam self-focusing is inevitable at the intensity levels involved in Raman stimulation. The following discussion, intended to illustrate the basic mechanisms at work, is not a sufficient basis for predicting or accounting for the performance of a Raman laser system, in which these complications are unavoidable.

The elementary circumstance which makes a medium Raman-active is a dependence of the molecular polarizability

$$\alpha = \varepsilon_0 \chi / N = \alpha_0 + (\partial\alpha/\partial x)x \tag{248}$$

on an internal coordinate $x$ of the molecule, one which can oscillate, having natural frequency $\omega_v$. The stiffness with which the dispersion electrons are bound varies with a change in this coordinate; an inverse effect must also exist, in which that part of the molecular system described by this coordinate is subject to a force in the presence of an electric field.

The charge polarization of a Raman medium containing $N$ independent molecules per unit volume has the form

$$P = N\alpha_0 E + x(\partial\alpha/\partial x)E = \varepsilon_0 \chi E + REx \tag{249}$$

(where $R$, a proportionality factor, is a measure of the Raman activity), and therefore it contains a component of Stokes frequency $\omega_1 - \omega_v$ when $x$ oscillates at $\omega_v$ and $E$ at $\omega_1$. This can generate a Stokes-frequency wave, however, only if the various oscillators are phased coherently, i.e., the molecules, although independent, are oscillating in a synchronized fashion. For this to be the case, the driving force which the electromagnetic field applies to the oscillators *via* the nonlinear polarizability must be sufficiently strong to impose order in what is normally a state of thermally disordered, uncoordinated oscillation. Otherwise, only statistical fluctuations contribute to Raman scattering, just, as we saw in Chapter 3, they produce the weak and incoherent Rayleigh scattering. The nonlinear driving force can be shown to be of second order in the electric field intensity; the total electric field comprises fundamental and Raman-shifted components, and its square therefore contains cross products; of these, the combination of $\omega_1$ (fundamental) and $\omega_S$ (Stokes) field components at the difference frequency $\omega_v$ acts in resonance on the molecular oscillators.

This situation can be described by two wave equations, one for fundamental and the other for Stokes light, coupled with an enormous number of forced-oscillator equations for the molecules. In the former, there are nonlinear coupling terms: $Rx^{(\omega_v)}E_S^{(\omega-\omega_v)}$ for the fundamental wave and $Rx^{(\omega_v)} \times E_1^{(\omega)}$ for the Stokes wave. In the oscillator equations, the driving terms contain the factors $RE_S^{(\omega-\omega_v)}E_1^{(\omega)}$; all the forced oscillator equations are identical except for a position-dependent phase factor, and may be represented by one typical equation.

Such sets of three coupled equations are by now familiar to the reader, who should at once recognize the possibility of exponential growth of the amplitudes of Stokes light and of molecular excitation, analogous to the growth of signal and idler waves in the parametric amplifier. The distinctive feature of the Raman amplifier is that instead of another light wave, an assemblage of driven molecular vibrations provides the means of coupling two light waves by modulating the nonlinear susceptibility. In fluids, the phase of these oscillators is established by that of the two interacting light beams rather than by propagation of a third wave. This feature eliminates the usually destructive role which dispersion plays in the case of three coupled light waves, so that index matching is automatically provided for the Stokes radiation if the optical branch of the mechanical dispersion curve is parallel to the $k$ axis.

From the fact that the Stokes beam interacting with the laser beam automatically establishes correct phasing of the molecular oscillators so as to ensure propagation of the Stokes beam, it follows that Raman gain is possible for any direction of propagation of the Stokes beam with respect to the fundamental. The greatest Stokes intensity should be observed from a Raman cell along the direction of its greatest illuminated length, unless some other considerations are introduced. Resonating the Stokes radiation by use of a Fabry–Perot mirror pair forces the molecular phasing to favor a few Stokes modes rather than the vast number predicted by Eq. (94). The mirrors can be placed with their axis transverse to the laser beam direction or parallel thereto. The Raman cell can be placed within the primary laser resonator.

Many Raman laser geometries are possible. Their common feature is the use of the primary laser beam as the pump, the Raman cell as a secondary laser medium, and a mode-selective resonator or cell geometry which exploits the intense superradiance to establish a preferred beam direction.

The exponential gain coefficient per unit length for the amplitude of Stokes radiation is proportional to the square of the fundamental amplitude. Until the latter begins to show appreciable depletion, the Stokes beam can grow exponentially in intensity, according to this simplified picture. It thus appears to originate near the end of the Raman cell. The practical complications introduced by beam self-focusing, by higher-order Raman shifts, by heating of the medium, and by the variation of intensity across a typical laser beam make quantitative relations of limited usefulness.

The multiply-downshifted, or higher-order, Stokes components can be suppressed, in principle at least, by absorption or by wavelength-selective filters, but not, of course, by index matching.

Many Raman-active media exist. Organic ring compounds (e.g., benzene, naphthalene, nitrobenzene, toluene, cyclohexane, bromonaphthalene) are particularly active. The Raman shifts are usually tabulated in $cm^{-1}$, as changes in the reciprocal of the wavelength.

The replacement of laser photons by Stokes photons of appreciably lower energy is accompanied by the generation of phonons which rapidly degrade into heat. Classically, this lost energy is expended by overcoming damping forces in the resonantly-driven molecular oscillators. This energy creates a perceptible temperature rise in the Raman cell.

Consider a benzene converter (Raman shift 3143 $cm^{-1}$) with a Nd-laser source ($\lambda = 1.06\,\mu$). A 200-J square pulse, if fully converted to first-order Stokes radiation, will generate at most 133 J at 7850 Å, the remaining 67 J appearing as heat in the cell, mostly in the last $e$-folding length.

Since the phonons will be emitted in the beam direction in an external converter cell, their momentum will be appreciable. When $Q$ joules are transferred in time $\tau$, the average force is $Q/c\tau$. Thus if the above pulse lasts for 10 nsec, a force of $F = 67(8) \div 3(8) = 22$ N will be exerted on the Raman liquid.

Thus, microscopic interactions on the molecules can, in the aggregate, constitute intense volume forces; this fact assists in understanding the strong coupling of light to acoustic waves, even though Raman activity need not be involved, in Brillouin scattering.

### 5.2.3. Anti-Stokes Rings.
In the ordinary Raman effect, few molecules are found in their excited state; e.g., with thermal equilibrium, only a fraction $\exp\{-\hbar\omega_v/kT\}$ are excited. The strong pumping action of a laser beam changes this situation drastically, so that an appreciable fraction of all molecules in the beam are soon made available for anti-Stokes emission. Classically, the anti-Stokes radiation is generated by interaction of the laser beam with molecular vibrations, but the phase of the latter is established by the still more intense Stokes radiation, and an index-matching requirement therefore exists for this three-wave process.

The phase of the molecular vibrations, that of the beat between fundamental and Stokes beams, is controlled by the wave factor $\exp i\{(k_S - k_1)z\}$. The beat between fundamental and anti-Stokes radiation must agree with that of the molecular vibrations. Hence for collinear beams

$$\exp i\{(k_1 - k_A)z\} = \exp i\{(k_S - k_1)z\}, \tag{250}$$

since $k_1 > k_A$, $k_S > k_1$. Unless $k_A$ can satisfy this requirement, a collinear anti-Stokes beam cannot exist. The curvature of the normal dispersion relations precludes it, in fact.

Quantum-mechanically, an anti-Stokes photon can be created at the expense of two laser photons and with the generation of a Stokes photon. The phonon is first emitted, then reabsorbed. The law of conservation of momentum requires that

$$\mathbf{k}_A + \mathbf{k}_S = 2\mathbf{k}_1, \tag{251}$$

which is consistent with the classical argument above, but more general. A direction can be found which satisfies this vector equation, but it confines the $S$ and $A$ photon pairs to conical beams coaxial with the laser beam. Figure 29 shows the required construction, the cones being generated by rotating the plane of the figure about $\mathbf{k}_1$.

By selecting this orientation for a secondary mirror pair as a Stokes resonator, one should expect to achieve an index match for the anti-Stokes radiation. A relationship of phase factors similar to Eq. (250) but taking account of the various beam directions,

$$\exp i\{(k_1 - k_A \cos \theta_A)z\} = \exp i\{(k_S \cos \theta - k_1)z\}, \tag{252}$$

establishes the phase of the molecular vibrations.

Many experiments designed to demonstrate this deduction and thus to produce strong anti-Stokes beams have shown that the true state of

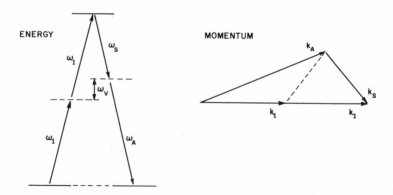

Figure 29. Energy and momentum balance for a possible stimulated Raman process in which both Stokes and anti-Stokes rings could be produced.

affairs is not simply representable by these relations. The higher-order Raman shifts, the self-focusing of the laser beam, and multimode interactions all greatly complicate the actual experiments. Raman-active media are especially liable to self-focusing. Moreover, there can be two-step processes as well as the one-step four-photon process of Figure 29. The mechanism is shown in Figure 30. The momentum diagram shows momentum-conserving phonons, not of the same direction, emitted in a Stokes process and absorbed in an anti-Stokes process. The phonon directions can be changed by intermolecular collisions, although the preponderant direction for the phonons is that which conserves momentum in the Stokes process. These phonons can stimulate further Stokes processes or be absorbed in anti-Stokes events.

### 5.2.4. The Inverse Raman Effect. The pumping action of the laser beam noted in the previous section affects the transparency of the medium. Assuming it to be normally transparent when unexposed, in the presence of strong laser radiation, it contains an appreciable population of molecules in vibrational states not normally accessible from the ground state. Light of frequency $\omega_S$ stimulates emission of more light of that frequency through conversion of laser-frequency photons with the aid of the molecular oscillators. It is therefore intensified. Light of frequency $\omega_A$, however, is absorbed, since it can be readily converted into molecular vibration quanta plus laser-frequency photons, the latter stimulating the process.

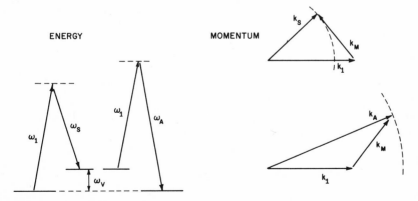

Figure 30. Energy and momentum conservation in independent Stokes and anti-Stokes Raman processes. The phonons required to conserve momentum are labeled $\mathbf{k}_M$ in the momentum diagrams. The Stokes process emits the phonon; the anti-Stokes process must absorb a phonon.

These effects are manifested when continuous radiation is passed through a Raman-active medium simultaneously irradiated by a laser. The usually transparent medium shows negative absorption at the Stokes line and reduced transmission at the anti-Stokes frequency.

A difficult experimental problem in demonstrating this effect is that of synchronizing the continuous radiation with the laser pulse. Both must be intense, but heating of the Raman liquid must be avoided. The spectrum of the continuum must be observed at the same time that the laser beam is passing. The best solution to these conflicting requirements is to obtain the "continuum" from a second Raman cell placed in the path of the laser beam between a lens and the experimental cell. The former produces Raman emission centered at the Stokes and anti-Stokes frequencies, but much broader than the superimposed absorption line at $\omega_A$ seen only with the second cell also present. The effect observed in this arrangement is somewhat analogous to the reversal of a broad emission line from a hot gas by absorption in the cooler outer parts of the gas, the broad Raman line being a satisfactory substitute for a continuum. This effect is capable of displaying the entire Raman spectrum of a substance and is intrinsically a high-speed spectroscopic tool which can be applied to study of transient components in rapid chemical reactions.

The energy diagram applying to this phenomenon is the reverse of that for the normal Raman effect (Figure 31).

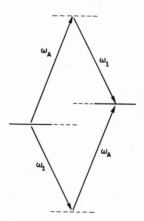

Figure 31. Energy diagram for the inverse Raman effect. Note that the laser photons $\omega_1$ are *emitted* rather than *absorbed* as in Figure 30, and the anti-Stokes frequency $\omega_A$ is absorbed.

### 5.2.5. Combinations of Harmonic and Raman Conversion.

The possibility of nearly complete conversion of a fundamental laser frequency to its second harmonic, together with that for Stokes downshifting, suggests their combination to generate coherent radiation at new frequencies.

The complete wavelength scale from the neodymium-laser second-harmonic at 5300 Å to the far-infrared can be covered by this method, at least in principle. The ruby-laser second-harmonic at 3470 Å is also available for Stokes downshifting, but a gap is left, roughly 1500 Å wide, between the Nd second harmonic and the greatest practical downshift of radiation which can be generated by ruby second harmonic in a Raman cell.

The latter is a consequence of the fixed amount of the Raman frequency shift, which becomes a decreasing fraction of the fundamental frequency as the latter is increased. The wavelength of $n$th-order Stokes-shifted Nth harmonic of a fundamental at $\lambda_1$ cm is

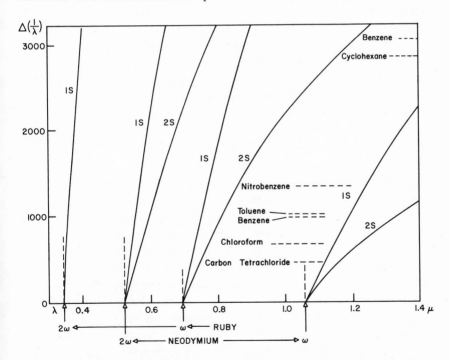

Figure 32. Wavelength of coherent radiation which can be generated by Raman laser action as a function of the Raman shift, tabulated in cm$^{-1}$. The primary laser beams are either ruby ($\lambda = 0.7\,\mu$) or neodymium ($\lambda = 1.06\,\mu$) or their respective second harmonics. The labels $1S$ and $2S$ on the various curves designate the order of Stokes downshifting involved. Some useful Raman media are indicated.

$$\lambda_{nN} = \lambda_1 (N - n\lambda_1 S)^{-1}, \tag{253}$$

where $S$ is the Stokes shift, $\omega_v/2\pi c$ cm$^{-1}$.

Figure 32 shows values of this quantity for fundamental and second harmonics of ruby and neodymium lasers. Various Raman media are indicated.

## 5.3. BRILLOUIN SCATTERING

### 5.3.1. The Classical Mechanism of Stimulated Brillouin Scattering. Brillouin scattering is describable entirely in classical terms, although, if we prefer, we can still describe it in terms of photons and phonons. This correspondence was presented in Section 3.4, where elementary relationships governing the scattering of light by acoustic waves were given, Eqs. (126)–(132). There it was shown how to relate the parameters of the incident and scattered light waves to those of the sound wave which by diffraction couples them, applying the Bragg law and the Doppler-shift formula of classical wave theory. It was also shown how, by introducing Planck's constant $\hbar$, these relations are converted into statements of conservation of energy and momentum for two photons and a phonon in a replacement process. Ordinary Brillouin scattering, first observed as the Debye–Sears effect, is regarded as spontaneous scattering. Stimulated scattering becomes important when the creation of phonons in the scattering process is so copious that it overcomes their loss by decay. The very high population of phonons then stimulates the emission process, the laser beam acting as a pump, transferring energy from the light beam to the sound wave. Quantum-mechanical analysis is not required to predict the coefficients of interaction. We prefer to speak of $\varepsilon$ rather than of $\chi$, since macroscopic, rather than microscopic, properties are involved.

The classical description has a more appealing "physical" content to the nonspecialist. There, the light wave creates pressure through electrostriction; the resultant density change affects the susceptibility. Thus light pumps the sound wave which scatters it; the scattering creates a second, frequency-shifted light wave, which constitutes the idler wave of a parametric amplifier.

To describe the interaction quantitatively, therefore, one writes three coupled wave equations, just as for the other nonlinear processes in earlier sections. Now, however, one of the three is an *acoustical* wave equation. All three contain driving terms originating in the nonlinear interactions, which couple the various waves.

The two electromagnetic waves have electric fields $E^{(\omega_1)}$, $E^{(\omega_2)}$ at, respectively, pump and idler frequencies. The sound wave is described by a Fourier component $\varrho^{(\omega_s)}$ of the density of the medium varying about the static value $\varrho_0$. The coupling arises from variation of the dielectric "constant" $\varepsilon$ with density. This takes the form of electrostriction in the acoustical wave equation. A Fourier component of electrostrictively produced pressure exists, varying at the difference frequency of pump and idler. This drives the sound wave at frequency

$$\omega_s = \omega_1 - \omega_2. \tag{254}$$

Simultaneously, a component of the charge polarization is made to vary at frequency $\omega_2$ by the interaction of the laser light with the medium, in which the sound wave causes the dielectric susceptibility to vary at its frequency $\omega_s$.

Similarly, the idler beam interacts with the acoustically-modulated susceptibility to provide the term in the fundamental wave equation which transfers its energy from the laser beam to sound and idler waves.

The Manley–Rowe conditions apply, as in other parametric amplifiers.

The threshold of the stimulation process is that beam power density of the laser beam at which the amplifying action of the parametric process overcomes the attenuation losses, leading to growth of sound and idler waves.

The following two sections analyze this phenomenon in a simplified situation.

## 5.3.2. Materials Properties Involved in Brillouin Scattering.

Consider a homogeneous, isotropic, dielectric fluid in which a laser beam of frequency $\omega_1$ is caused to undergo Brillouin scattering by diffraction from a sound wave, producing a scattered "idler" wave of frequency $\omega_2$. Equation (128) relates these frequencies to the scattering angle $\theta$, index of refraction $\nu$, and velocity of sound $v_s$.

Besides the index of refraction or dielectric constant, the relevant intrinsic properties of the medium are the adiabatic bulk modulus of elasticity $\beta$, the attenuation factors, $\alpha_s$ for sound waves and $\alpha$ for light transmission, and the coefficient of electrostriction $\gamma$.

The first relates the sound pressure $p$ to associated variations in the density $\varrho$, and is defined by

$$\beta = \varrho \, \partial p / \partial \varrho. \tag{255}$$

As an example, the equation of state of an ideal gas (in which Brillouin scattering is possible) proves the bulk modulus equal to the pressure in slow, isothermal compressions, but higher by a factor $c_p/c_v$ * for rapid variations, as in the passage of sound; then there is no time for heat of compression to flow before arrival of the succeeding rarefaction. The elasticity and density of the fluid determine the velocity of transmission $v_s$ of sound waves, which exhibits dispersion, as noted in Section 5.1.4, because of the rate-dependence of $\beta$.

Parenthetically, we remark at this point that measurements of $v_s$ at very high frequencies (short wavelength) are helpful in testing knowledge of the equation of state of a fluid or of the structure of a solid. Brillouin scattering is an excellent source of ultra-high-frequency sound for this research.

The coefficient of electrostriction is defined by the relation of dielectric constant to density

$$\gamma = \tfrac{1}{2}\varrho \, \partial\varepsilon/\partial\varrho. \tag{256}$$

This coefficient does not in general vanish; an increase in density increases the number of polarizable electronic systems in a unit volume. However, the footnote on p. 41 remarks that the effective field within a dielectric which creates the molecular dipoles, is not the total electric field, that their ratio is structure-dependent, and that $\varepsilon$ is therefore not strictly proportional to density. In fact, substances with negative values of $\gamma$ exist.

It was noted in Section 3.7 that body forces accompany the action of the field on the polarization.

The energy stored in the electric field, according to Eq. (4), is

$$U = \tfrac{1}{2}\varepsilon E^2. \tag{257}$$

Suppose the density varies, as in a sound wave. Since the dielectric constant $\varepsilon$ changes with it, the electrical energy is changed; energy must therefore be transferred between the electric and the acoustic fields, in the amount

$$dU = \tfrac{1}{2}E^2 \, d\varepsilon = \gamma E^2 \, d\varrho/\varrho. \tag{258}$$

Conversely, establishing or changing an electric field creates mechanical strain. This is electrostriction. The electrostrictive pressure in fluids is

---

* The ratio of the specific heat measured at constant pressure to that at constant volume; their difference represents the energy required for expansion, and $c_v$ is determined by the number of degrees of freedom of the molecules.

$$P_{\text{el}} = \tfrac{1}{2}\gamma E^2. \tag{259}$$

In solids, the relationship is not simple.

The role of the attenuation constant will become clear shortly.

The fluid necessarily obeys a continuity condition; steady motion can take place at constant density, but in an acoustic field, where a velocity gradient exists, there must be a compensating density change, and conversely. Suppose that the local velocity **u** is in the direction of propagation of the soundwave, say in the $Z$ direction. Then continuity requires that at every point,

$$\frac{\partial u}{\partial z} + \frac{1}{\varrho}\,\frac{\partial \varrho}{\partial t} = 0. \tag{260}$$

None of the optical nonlinearities considered previously is assumed to be present. Of course, they can be, and this can greatly complicate matters, particularly in the case of beam self-focusing.

### 5.3.3. Electrostrictively Driven Sound Waves. Consider

now a small volume element in the fluid having length $dx$, width $dy$, and extension $dz$ along the direction of the sound wave (Figure 33). The pressures

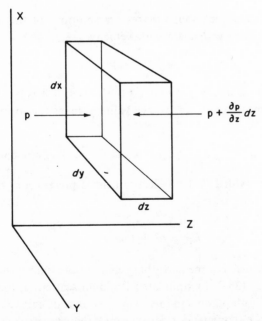

Figure 33. Volume element for derivation of the acoustical wave equation, showing pressures acting on opposite sides to exert net force in the $X$ direction.

applied on opposite sides would balance were it not for the sound wave and the fields of the light waves. The motion is opposed by frictional forces proportional to velocity.

Applying Newton's second law to the mass $\varrho\, dx\, dy\, dz$ within the volume element,

$$dx\, dy\left[p - \left(p + \frac{\partial p}{\partial z}\, dz\right)\right] - gu\, dx\, dy\, dz = \frac{\partial u}{\partial t}\, \varrho\, dx\, dy\, dz \qquad (261)$$

or

$$-gu - \frac{\partial p}{\partial z} - \varrho\, \frac{\partial u}{\partial t} = 0. \qquad (262)$$

The pressure in Eq. (262) contains both the ordinary hydrodynamic and the electrostrictive contributions.

Differentiating with respect to $z$, applying the continuity condition, Eq. (260), and introducing the compressibility and electrostrictive pressure relations of the previous section, this becomes a damped wave equation with a nonlinear driving term,

$$\frac{\partial^2 \varrho}{\partial z^2} = \frac{1}{v_s^2}\, \frac{\partial^2 \varrho}{\partial t^2} + \frac{g}{\beta}\, \frac{\partial \varrho}{\partial t} - \frac{\gamma}{2v_s^2}\, \frac{\partial^2 E^2}{\partial z^2}. \qquad (263)$$

Ordinary undamped sound waves are solutions of this equation with $E = 0$, $g = 0$. They propagate with velocity

$$v_s = (\beta/\varrho_0)^{1/2}. \qquad (264)$$

The resistance factor $g$ attenuates the waves; if it is not too large, the variation of density about its average value $\varrho_0$ takes the form of a damped wave. Thus

$$\varrho^{(\omega_s)} - \varrho = \tfrac{1}{2}\varrho_s \exp\{i(\omega_s t - k_s z) - \alpha_s z\} + \text{comp. conj.} \qquad (265)$$

is a solution, provided that no electric field is present and that

$$\alpha_s = g/2\varrho \qquad (266)$$

$$k_s^2 = \alpha^2 + (\omega_s^2/v_s^2). \qquad (267)$$

We are interested in the perturbing effect of the third term on the right-hand side of Eq. (263). In stimulated Brillouin scattering, the total field $E$ is composed of both pump and idler waves, so that its square contains cross products at sum and difference frequencies. Of these we are interested only in the synchronous term at the difference frequency, which drives the sound wave.

## 5.3.4. Acoustically Modulated Light Waves.
Writing electromagnetic wave equations for the fields $E^{(\omega_1)}$ and $E^{(\omega_2)}$ completes the formal description of the parametric interaction. These also contain coupling terms, because of the acoustical variation of the dielectric constant about its normal value $v^2$:

$$\varepsilon = v^2 + [2\gamma(\varrho^{(\omega_s)} - \varrho_0)/\varrho_0]. \qquad (268)$$

We shall illustrate the application to collinear waves in what follows.

Making the appropriate modification of the electromagnetic wave equation, for instance, of Eq. (85), one obtains for the fundamental wave

$$\frac{\partial^2 E^{(\omega_1)}}{\partial z^2} = \frac{v^2}{c^2} \frac{\partial^2 E^{(\omega_1)}}{\partial t^2} - \frac{2\gamma}{c^2 \varrho_0} \frac{\partial^2}{\partial t^2} (\varrho^{(\omega_s)} E^{(\omega_2)})^{(\omega_1)} \qquad (269)$$

by retaining only synchronous nonlinear terms. Similarly, the idler wave obeys

$$\frac{\partial^2 E^{(\omega_2)}}{\partial z^2} = \frac{v^2}{c^2} \frac{\partial^2 E^{(\omega_2)}}{\partial t^2} + \frac{2\gamma}{c^2 \varrho_0} \frac{\partial^2}{\partial t^2} (\varrho^{(\omega_s)} E^{(\omega_1)})^{(\omega_2)} \qquad (270)$$

and the acoustic wave, if damping is negligible, obeys

$$\frac{\partial^2 \varrho^{(\omega_s)}}{\partial z^2} = \frac{1}{v_s^2} \frac{\partial^2 \varrho^{(\omega_s)}}{\partial t^2} - \frac{\gamma}{2v_s^2} \frac{\partial^2}{\partial z^2} (E^{(\omega_1)} E^{(\omega_2)})^{(\omega_s)}. \qquad (271)$$

Applying the perturbation method, we first find solutions of these equations without the interaction terms, next substitute these back in the complete wave equations as first-order approximations in the coupling terms, and, finally, determine their effect on the amplitudes of the respective waves.

The zero-order solutions are

$$E^{(\omega_1)} = \tfrac{1}{2} A_1 \exp i\{\omega_1 t - k_1 z\} + \text{comp. conj.}, \qquad (272)$$

$$E^{(\omega_2)} = \tfrac{1}{2} A_2 \exp i\{\omega_2 t - k_2 z\} + \text{comp. conj.}, \qquad (273)$$

$$\varrho^{(\omega_s)} = \tfrac{1}{2} \varrho_s \exp i\{\omega_s t - k_s z\} + \text{comp. conj.}. \qquad (274)$$

In next order of approximation, the amplitudes vary with $z$.

The important case is that of a strong laser beam. Assuming $A_1$ and $\bar{A}_1$ constant, and carrying out the usual algebraic steps, we obtain

$$d\varrho_s/dz = -i\gamma k_s A_1 \bar{A}_2 / 8 v_s^2, \qquad (275)$$

$$d\bar{A}_2/dz = i\gamma \omega_2 \varrho_s \bar{A}_1 / 2 \varrho_0 c, \qquad (276)$$

which can be combined

$$d^2\varrho_s/dz^2 = (\gamma^2 k_s k_2 A_1 \bar{A}_1/16\beta\nu)\varrho_s = K^2\varrho_s. \tag{277}$$

## 5.3.5. Requirements for Combined Wave Amplification. 
The solution of Eq. (277) is a growing sound wave which, at large distances, grows exponentially:

$$\varrho_s = C \sinh Kz + D \cosh Kz. \tag{278}$$

To determine the arbitrary constants $C$ and $D$, we must also find the idler wave, by substituting Eq. (278) into Eq. (276) and integrating:

$$\bar{A}_2 = \frac{i\gamma\omega_2 \bar{A}_1}{2\varrho_0 cK} (C \cosh Kz + D \sinh Kz). \tag{279}$$

These suggest that some initial amplitude must exist in either sound or idler wave, or both, if the amplification process is to start. This is provided by thermally-excited fluctuations of density in the medium, so that no provision is necessary to introduce an initial idler signal. The constant $D$ then has a small initial value, and even when $C$ vanishes, the waves grow rapidly, with an $e$-folding distance given by $K^{-1}$.

To evaluate these formulas, we need to know the material constants. Suppose the medium to be air at normal pressure. The refractive index is unity. The electrostriction constant has the same dimensions and value comparable with $\varepsilon_0$. The effective bulk modulus is the pressure times the specific heat ratio, 1.40. Hence approximate values are

$$\nu = 1,$$
$$\gamma \doteq \varepsilon_0 = 8.85(-12) \text{ C/V-m}$$
$$\beta = 1.4(5) \text{ J/m}^3,$$
$$\varrho_0 = 1.3 \text{ kg/m}^3,$$
$$\nu_s = 3.3(2) \text{ m/sec.}$$

Using a ruby laser,

$$\lambda_1 = 0.7(-6) \text{ m}$$
$$k_1 = 9(6) \text{ m}^{-1}.$$

Backscattering this light changes $k$ only slightly (small Doppler shift, $\nu_s \ll c$), but it generates sound with propagation constant (wave number) of double this value, or

$$k_s = k_1 - (-k_2) \doteq 2k_1$$
$$= 1.8(7) \text{ m}^{-1}$$

and frequency

$$\omega_s = k_s v_s = 5.9(9) \text{ sec}^{-1}$$

in the far-ultrasonic range.

The growth coefficient is found by evaluating Eq. (277). Rewriting it slightly,

$$K^2 \doteq (k_s k_2 \varepsilon_0 / 8\beta v c)(\tfrac{1}{2}\varepsilon_0 c A_1 \bar{A}_1), \tag{280}$$

to separate out the laser beam power density, we obtain

$$K^2 \doteq 0.43(-11) \times \text{ beam power density in W/m}^2. \tag{281}$$

Since power densities of tens of megawatts per square *centimeter* are easily available, we can hope to observe traveling-wave amplification. However, as in Raman processes, there is a threshold power requirement. Moreover, the self-focusing effect is often a complicating factor at these beam intensities.

When damping is included in the analysis, one obtains the threshold for stimulation by requiring that

$$K^2 > \alpha_s \alpha. \tag{282}$$

A threshold is apparent from Eq. (257); the driving term must exceed the damping term (which we later ignored) if the sound wave is to grow.

Note that a common index of refraction $v$ applies to pump and idler. The actual frequency shift is extremely small, of course, because of the great disparity between wave velocities for light and sound, even in rigid, dense solids.

Because of this small frequency shift, the pump and idler can be resonated within a single Fabry–Perot mirror system. In such a resonator, a focused optical beam is not necessary to obtain an effect, the threshold power density then being reduced by several orders of magnitude. Index matching is not required, and, as in Raman scattering, gain can occur in any direction, so an off-axis resonator can be used to select the direction of light scattering in order to establish a particular direction and frequency for the sound wave which is to be produced. The latter can be tuned by varying the inclination of the second axis.

The ratio of phonon to photon energy is small, of the order of $v_s/c$, and the highest value of the energy which can be fed from the light into the sound wave is this fraction of the energy of the incident light. Nevertheless, the generation of monochromatic sound waves, coherently, with a power density of hundreds of kilowatts per square centimeter in pulses lasting only a few nanoseconds is a spectacular as well as useful phenomenon. This energy rapidly degrades into heat, and, in solids, it can permanently damage the region near a laser-beam focal point.

## 5.4. INTERACTIONS OF LIGHT WITH FREE ELECTRONS

In all the nonlinear optical processes so far described, the electric field of a light wave has acted upon electrons bound in atomic or crystal structures, and the nature of their binding has determined the resulting effect on the field of the light wave.

Electrons are not always bound, however. In plasmas, although free, they are subject to fluctuating fields of ions and small departures from local equality of ion and electron charge densities, in the form of periodic variations at well-defined frequencies, called "plasma oscillations." The characteristic electron frequency is

$$\omega_p = (N_e e^2/m\varepsilon_0)^{1/2}, \qquad (283)$$

where $e$ is the electron charge, $m$ its mass, and $N_e$ the electron concentration.

Raman-like interaction is possible, the plasma frequency playing the same role as $\omega_v$ in Section 5.2. Measuring the resulting Stokes shift is one way in which one can determine $N_e$ of a plasma with a laser beam probe.

In metals, electrons in the conduction band pass freely, but are stopped at surfaces, where only extremely intense fields can extract them. Laser beams can do so; the local heating which accompanies the process greatly complicates efforts to understand it, however. The usual result is exploding metal vapor and some plasma. Thermionic emission and multiphoton photoelectric emission (of which the classical equivalent is called field emission) are both present, but optical absorption is the principal effect. At lower intensities, the metallic electrons at a surface (which lacks inversion symmetry) can be caused to generate second harmonic in the reflected laser beam.

In vacuum tubes and accelerators, one can obtain electrons which are for all practical purposes free. These can scatter light. It is not possible for a photon to be absorbed by a free electron; conservation of energy and momentum cannot be simultaneously satisfied unless a secondary photon is left after the event. At low energies, the process is called Thomson scattering; for photons of relativistic energies, it is called the Compton effect. A significant characteristic of the latter process is a perceptible change in the energy of the scattered photon. The electron, initially practically at rest, recoils, diminishing the energy of the photon. In scattering of low-energy photons, the electrons have thermal spreads in energy considerably greater than the maximum possible recoil, and when in a beam, have directed motion. These can change the energy of the photons scattered by them, the thermal motion broadening and the directed motion displacing the scattered spectral line.

Experiments have been reported in which electron beams have been bombarded with laser beams, producing Doppler-shifted scattered light. With low electron energy, these are not particularly exciting. However, when the electron beam is moving at relativistic speeds, as in a particle accelerator, the energy of a backscattered photon is extremely high. For example, 100-Mev electrons can scatter 1.78-eV laser photons as X-ray photons of 300-kV energy; at 1 Gev, the photons are scattered as 28-Mev radiation.

This is a process which converts visible light, or even infrared light, to X rays! Unfortunately, the scattered light is incoherent because the electrons are not correlated in positions or velocity, and better ways exist for generating X rays.

The inverse process is the scattering of electrons by light. The possibility of stimulated Compton scattering, as this has been called, was realized as long ago as 1932, although it was also realized that it should be very difficult to observe. Recently, very careful attempts have been reported to observe the effect. An electron beam was directed at the standing electromagnetic wave pattern in a laser cavity at the nearly glancing incidence required for Bragg reflections, and deflections of the electrons were sought which should indicate that they were being diffracted by the light wave field, just as light is diffracted by sound and *vice versa* in stimulated Brillouin scattering. This experiment has proved very difficult because of many spurious effects associated with the laser pulse. Although many deflections of electrons at the correct angle were observed, the existence of stimulated Compton scattering has yet to be conclusively established.

## 5.5. OPTICAL NONLINEARITY IN GASES

### 5.5.1. The Nonlinear Susceptibility of a Gas.

Except in the sections on Brillouin scattering, the optical media of concern to us in our discussion of nonlinear optics have been solids, usually crystalline, or liquids. Being of relatively low density, gases have only very small nonlinear terms in their susceptibility. All have third-order terms, and many, in which the molecules lack inversion symmetry, have second-order nonlinearity. A simple example of the latter is methane, $CH_4$; its molecule has a central carbon atom with four symmetrically disposed hydrogen atoms occupying the corners of a tetrahedral structure, which has no center of inversion.

We can accordingly expect to produce second and third harmonics with moderately intense laser beams in gases. However, gas molecules are not fixed in position or orientation, as are the unit cells of solids. There is accordingly no way in which one can arrange for the light which they scatter to be combined coherently. Only the fluctuations in local density, by giving rise to Rayleigh scattering by precluding destructive interference, can make the harmonic generation observable.

Raman interactions of gases are relatively more interesting than harmonic generation, because the Stokes scattering is coherent. Raman spectroscopy of gases is a useful research technique, using gas lasers as sources of primary radiation.

At higher beam powers, electrostriction becomes important, causing not only stimulated Brillouin scattering, but also nonlinearity in the refractive index and the attendant complications of beam self-focusing.

The most spectacular effect is plasma formation, or electrical breakdown, a subject which has proved difficult to explain quantitatively.

### 5.5.2. Observations of Breakdown in Gases.

A typical setup for studying the behavior of gases under intense optical irradiation might consist of a Q-switched ruby laser, giving intensities of the order of 50 MW lasting about 30 nsec, with a lens serving as the window into a gas cell. The latter is filled with a gas under study to a desired pressure, which can be varied. The radiation passes through a focal region in the gas, which, with good lens quality and a pure laser mode, could be of the order of a few wavelengths in diameter, but is usually considerably greater.

It thereafter diverges, passing through an exit window to a photodetector.

If, at a fixed gas pressure, the laser excitation is increased on successive shots, the full intensity is transmitted until a very sharply defined threshold level is reached, just above which only half of the laser pulse is transmitted

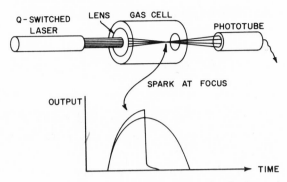

Figure 34. Electrical breakdown of a gas by the focused
beam of a laser.

(Figure 34). The second half of the pulse is cut off abruptly. Simultaneously, a spark appears at the focal point in the gas.

The power density required for breakdown is of the order of 6(15) W/cm². This is a field intensity of 1.5(9) V/m, which is only 0.15 V/Å; this field seems very low indeed to produce ionization by direct action on the bound electrons.

The phenomenon appears even more mysterious when one considers the small size of the focal volume and inquires as to the probability of finding a stray free electron there which could be accelerated to ionizing energy. This consideration seems incompatible with the observation that breakdown occurs *invariably* on every pulse of greater than threshold intensity.

A further source of perplexity is the relatively weak dependence of the threshold field on the ionization potential of the gas. Helium and argon, ionization potentials respectively 24.5 and 15.7 V, break down at optical field strengths which are within a factor of two of each other. A mechanism involving ionization by the high-energy tail of an electron energy distribution heated by the field of the light wave would predict a difference of many orders of magnitude for these gases, and could not account for the abrupt thresholds.

The charge liberated by ionization within the spark can be collected by means of a pair of electrodes symmetrically disposed on either side of the focal point. Typical values of 1(13) electron–ion pairs are found at atmospheric pressure. To effect this should require absorption of about 5(−4) J, a very small fraction of the total energy, about 1 J, of the laser pulse. The rest of the energy is converted to some other form, after the spark has occurred, by the gas or plasma in the focal volume. Most of it appears ultimately as a pressure rise in the gas. The mechanism cannot be Brillouin scattering alone, as the focal volume is too small and the medium too tenuous, and the opacity of the plasma spot is a direct and prompt consequence of its formation. Very little scattered radiation is observed at the laser wavelength, but the focal volume does emit intense blackbody radiation.

As the laser power is increased, the ionized region moves closer to the lens. This can be understood as a consequence of the rapidity of ionization, the sharp threshold level, and the opacity of the ionized region.

It has been facetiously observed that this is an extreme case of frequency conversion, from laser frequency to white.

### 5.5.3. Theories of Gas Breakdown by Laser Beams.

The breakdown of gases at microwave frequencies has been satisfactorily explained, although the direct data on the collision cross sections of electrons needed to provide their full quantitative verification are lacking. Moreover, the photoionization of atoms by very-short-wavelength radiation having photon energy well above the ionization energy is fairly well understood. Explanation is more difficult in the optical region.

In the microwave case, the quantum energy is low; the excitation of electrons by the field of the wave is analyzed classically as a continuous process of acceleration, interrupted by random collisions with gas molecules.

The optical case, with photon energy 1.78 eV, cannot properly be treated in this manner. To reach ionizing energy, eight light quanta must be absorbed and transferred to an atom in the case of argon, 14 in the case of helium. These numbers are too low to justify the continuous interaction assumed by the usual microwave breakdown theory. Discreteness is an essential feature.

Attempts have therefore been made to modify the microwave theories. Each overlooks a very essential question by assuming that a free electron of thermal energy will always be available within the minute focal volume. In the field of a nearby atom or ion, an electron is not entirely free, but lies in an energy state of the continuum above the ionization limit for that compound system, moving with kinetic energy insufficient to ionize other atoms with which it collides. The interaction with an atom or ion is a necessary condition for photon absorption by the electron, since a completely free electron cannot absorb a photon. The atom or ion allows momentum to be conserved, so that a series of absorption steps can occur, the electron acquiring ionizing energy after a sufficient number of photons have been absorbed.

An early "inverse-bremsstrahlung" model assumes that this process transfers enough energy to the unbound electron to enable it to excite high-lying states in atoms with which it collides; the resulting excited atoms can then be ionized by two-photon absorption, completing the process; the free electron population then grows rapidly. In later versions, the entire process of ionization is by impact of electrons which have been accelerated by inverse bremsstrahlung.

The inverse-bremsstrahlung mechanism fails to explain the sharp threshold and the inevitability and completeness of breakdown once it is exceeded. It is indeed amazing that one can *always* find a free electron in a gas of high ionization potential within so small a focal volume; that electron must be liberated by the action of the radiation!

The mystery of nucleation of the electron population is resolved by calculation of the probability of direct photoionization by simultaneous absorption of $N$ (eight in the case of Ar, 14 by He) photons from the radiation field. To do this, one must resort to $N$th-order perturbation theory. Two circumstances turn out to have an important effect on this calculation: In the expressions of $N$th-order perturbation theory for the transition amplitude, there is a sum of products of $N$ resonance denominators containing differences between integer multiples of the photon energy and known states of the atoms. In all of the noble gases, there are states whose energy values happen to make the corresponding resonance factors very high.

Moreover, in the final expression for the ionization cross section, the photon flux appears raised to the $(N - 1)$th power. This factor varies so rapidly (13th power in the case of helium) with laser beam power that the remaining factors in the expression need not be known precisely. Even with an error of four orders of magnitude in the matrix elements, this theory still predicts the ionization threshold to within a factor of five. The very high power of the photon flux or power level which appears in the formula accounts for the very sharp threshold observed experimentally.

# APPENDIX. FREE AND FORCED OSCILLATIONS IN SLIGHTLY NONLINEAR SYSTEMS

## 1. LINEAR OSCILLATOR

Free vibrations of linear oscillators are solutions of the equation

$$y'' + gy' + \omega_0^2 y = 0, \tag{A1}$$

which is satisfied by

$$y \doteq y_1 e^{-gt/2} \cos\{\omega t - \phi\}, \tag{A2}$$

a damped vibration which, if the damping is small, occurs very nearly at the natural frequency, $\omega \doteq \omega_0$.

Forced vibrations of a linear oscillator occur at the driving frequency; the differential equation describing a multiply-periodic forced oscillation,

$$y'' + gy' + \omega_0^2 y = \sum_i E_i \cos\{\omega_i t\}, \tag{A3}$$

has the steady-state solution

$$y = \sum_i y_i \cos\{\omega_i t - \phi_i\}, \tag{A4}$$

where

$$y_i = \frac{E_i}{[(\omega_i^2 - \omega_0^2)^2 + \omega_i^2 g^2]^{1/2}} \tag{A5}$$

is the amplitude of the $i$th Fourier component and

$$\phi_i = \tan^{-1} \frac{g\omega_i}{\omega_i^2 - \omega_0^2} \tag{A6}$$

is the phase lag between driving force and the $i$th Fourier component of the displacement; it vanishes if there is negligible damping.

## 2. PERTURBATION METHOD FOR TREATING SMALL NONLINEARITIES

Nonlinearities encountered in optical problems are as a rule confined to second- and third-order terms with very small coefficients. The general equation for a free nonlinear oscillator with small second- and third-order terms is

$$y'' + gy' + \omega_0^2 y + a_2 y^2 + a_3 y^3 = 0. \tag{A7}$$

The condition

$$\omega_0^2 y \gg a_2 y^2, a_3 y^3 \tag{A8}$$

allows one to employ a perturbation method of solution. The exact solution for $y$ will not differ greatly from that found in Section 1. It will be called the zero-order solution. The first-order solution is obtained by solving the equation resulting from substitution of Eq. (A2) into Eq. (A7), which then has the form of an equation of forced oscillation.

## 3. FREE OSCILLATION WITH SMALL NONLINEARITIES OF SECOND AND THIRD ORDER

To illustrate the principle of the method simply, we first apply it to the undamped, free oscillator. The first-order equation for free vibrations

$$y'' + \omega_0^2 y = -a_2 y_1^2 \cos^2\{\omega_1 t\} - a_3 y_1^3 \cos^3\{\omega_1 t\} \tag{A9}$$

can be transformed, using the identities

$$2\cos^2 \theta = 1 + \cos 2\theta, \tag{A10}$$

$$4\cos^3 \theta = \cos 3\theta + 3\cos \theta, \tag{A11}$$

into

$$
\begin{aligned}
y'' + \omega_0^2 y = &-\tfrac{1}{2}a_2 y_1^2 - \tfrac{1}{4}3a_3 y_1^3 \cos\{\omega_1 t\} \\
&-\tfrac{1}{2}a_2 y_1^2 \cos\{2\omega_1 t\} - \tfrac{1}{4}a_3 y_1^3 \cos\{3\omega_1 t\},
\end{aligned} \tag{A12}
$$

containing one constant and three harmonic driving terms. The first-order solution must therefore be

$$y = y_0 + y_1 \cos\{\omega_1 t\} + y_2 \cos\{2\omega_1 t\} + y_3 \cos\{3\omega_1 t\}. \tag{A13}$$

By substitution and comparison of coefficients, it is found that

$$y_0 = -a_2 y_1^2 / 2\omega_0^2, \tag{A14}$$

$$\omega_1^2 = \omega_0^2 + (3a_3 y_1^2 / 4), \tag{A15}$$

$$y_2 = -a_2 y_1^2 / 2(\omega_0^2 - 4\omega_1^2), \tag{A16}$$

$$y_3 = -a_3 y_1^3 / 4(\omega_0^2 - 9\omega_1^2), \tag{A17}$$

so that the second-order term displaces the center of vibration and the third-order term increases the fundamental frequency by a small amount

$$\omega_1 - \omega_0 \doteq 3a_3 y_1^2 / 8\omega_0 \tag{A18}$$

dependent on the square of the amplitude of the fundamental. The displacement

$$y \doteq -(a_2 / 2\omega_0^2) y_1^2 + y_1 \cos\{\omega_1 t\} + (a_2 / 6\omega_0^2) y_1^2 \cos\{2\omega_1 t\}$$
$$+ (a_3 / 8\omega_0^2) y_1^3 \cos\{3\omega_1 t\}, \tag{A19}$$

contains second and third harmonics as well as the fundamental frequency component.

In the next order of approximation, this solution is substituted in the original differential equation (A9) to form a new differential equation, leading to a more refined solution, containing still higher harmonics.

The dc and second-harmonic components in Eq. (A19) are both proportional to $a_2$; this coefficient does not appear in the third-harmonic component. It is therefore permissible to treat the effect of each order of nonlinearity separately. This is further justified in practice by the experimental circumstance that when second-order nonlinearity can occur at all, the second harmonic can be made far more intense than the third harmonic. Moreover, index-matching techniques allow suppression of all but one of the several harmonics which may arise in optical media.

## 4. SECOND-ORDER NONLINEAR OSCILLATOR IN FORCED VIBRATION

We accordingly consider next the forced oscillator with only second-order nonlinearity,

$$y'' + gy' + \omega_0^2 y + a_2 y^2 = E_0 \cos\{\omega t\}. \tag{A20}$$

The displacement, given in lowest order by

$$y = y_1 \cos\{\omega t + \phi\}, \tag{A21}$$

is used to approximate $y$ in the second-order term, $a_2y^2$. The resulting equation is satisfied by the solution

$$y = y_0 + y_1 \cos\{\omega t + \phi\} + y_2 \cos\{2(\omega t + \phi)\}, \qquad (A22)$$

in which

$$y_0 = -a_2 y_1^2/2\omega_0^2, \qquad (A23)$$

$$y_1 = E_0/[(\omega^2 - \omega_0^2)^2 - g^2\omega^2]^{1/2}, \qquad (A24)$$

$$y_2 = a_2 y_1^2/2(4\omega^2 - \omega_0^2), \qquad (A25)$$

$$\phi = \tan^{-1}[-g\omega/(\omega_0^2 - \omega^2)]. \qquad (A26)$$

When $\omega \gg \omega_0$ and damping is negligible, these approximate to

$$y_0 = -a_2 y_1^2/2\omega_0^2 = -a_2 E_0^2/2\omega_0^2\omega^2, \qquad (A27)$$

$$y_1 = E_0/\omega^2, \qquad (A28)$$

$$y_2 = a_2 y_1^2/8\omega^2 = a_2 E_0^2/8\omega^6. \qquad (A29)$$

At resonance, the damping directly determines the fundamental amplitude and indirectly determines the amplitude of the second harmonic by determining the applicable value of $y_1$.

Higher orders of approximation lead to fourth, sixth, etc., harmonics, but no experimental need for this refinement has yet arisen in optics, as the intensities are extremely weak, and it is unlikely that special index-matching techniques will be possible to enhance them, because of dispersion.

## 5. THIRD-ORDER NONLINEARITY IN FORCED VIBRATION

Third-order nonlinearity is next considered for an undamped oscillator. This is adequate except near resonance, as it corresponds in optics to the region of normal dispersion. We shall not require a phase difference $\phi$. The differential equation

$$y'' + \omega_0^2 y + a_3 y^3 = E_0 \cos\{\omega t\} \qquad (A30)$$

has the approximate solution

$$y = [E_0/(\omega_0^2 - \omega^2)] \cos\{\omega t\}, \qquad (A31)$$

so that it is very nearly equivalent to the linear equation

$$y'' + \omega_0^2 y = E_0 \cos\{\omega t\} - \frac{a_3 E_0^2}{4(\omega_0^2 - \omega^2)^3} [\cos\{3\omega t\} + 3 \cos\{\omega t\}], \quad \text{(A32)}$$

and so is satisfied by

$$y = y_1 \cos\{\omega t\} + y_3 \cos\{3\omega t\}, \quad \text{(A33)}$$

in which, by comparing coefficients of $\cos\{\omega t\}$ and $\cos\{3\omega t\}$, it is found that

$$y_1 = \frac{E_0}{\omega_0^2 - \omega^2} \left[ 1 - \frac{3}{4} \frac{a_3 E_0^2}{(\omega_0^2 - \omega^2)^2} \right], \quad \text{(A34)}$$

$$y_3 = -\frac{a_3 y_1}{4} \frac{E_0^2}{9\omega^2 - \omega_0^2}. \quad \text{(A35)}$$

When driving frequency $\omega$ is far below the resonance frequency,

$$y_1 \doteq E_0/\omega_0^2, \quad \text{(A36)}$$

$$y_3 \doteq a_3 E_0^3/4\omega_0^2. \quad \text{(A37)}$$

When $\omega$ is much higher than resonance,

$$y_1 \doteq -E_0/\omega^2, \quad \text{(A38)}$$

$$y_3 \doteq -a_3 E_0^3/36\omega_0^2 \omega_1^2. \quad \text{(A39)}$$

Iteration of this solution, to obtain a more refined approximation, is not necessary in optics, for reasons already given.

## 6. SECOND-ORDER NONLINEAR OSCILLATOR WITH TWO IMPRESSED FREQUENCIES

This problem is more general. The differential equation is

$$y'' + \omega_0^2 y + a_2 y^2 = E_1 \cos\{\omega_1 t\} + E_2 \cos\{\omega_2 t\} \quad \text{(A40)}$$

with zero-order solution

$$y = \frac{E_1}{\omega_0^2 - \omega_1^2} \cos\{\omega_1 t\} + \frac{E_2}{\omega_0^2 - \omega_2^2} \cos\{\omega_2 t\}$$
$$= y_1 \cos\{\omega_1 t\} + y_2 \cos\{\omega_2 t\}, \quad \text{(A41)}$$

the square of which is

$$y^2 = \tfrac{1}{2}y_1{}^2[1 + \cos\{2\omega_1 t\}] + \tfrac{1}{2}y_2{}^2[1 + \cos\{2\omega_2 t\}]$$
$$+ y_1 y_2 [\cos\{(\omega_1 + \omega_2)t\} + \cos\{(\omega_1 - \omega_2)t\}]. \qquad (A42)$$

In addition to the two fundamentals, two second harmonics and their combined dc effect, sum and difference frequencies appear in the solution. If the amplitudes and frequencies of the two forcing terms are such that they produce comparable fundamental amplitudes, the mixture terms are comparable in importance with the harmonics. One of them may produce the dominant effect if its frequency is near resonance. The dispersion of the medium assumes even greater importance when index-matching is considered.

Physically, one can regard the phenomenon as a consequence of nonlinear response to the beats between the unequal impressed frequencies. The generation of combination tones by the ear and the action of super-heterodyne detection circuits are well-known examples of this phenomenon.

A single fundamental may be considered to beat with itself at sum (double) and difference (zero) frequencies. The second-harmonic and dc effects are therefore special cases of this problem.

This can be generalized to any number of impressed frequencies and to higher orders of nonlinearity, with an increasingly complex spectrum of oscillations in the response.

# BIBLIOGRAPHY

Included here are sources which were found to be useful in the preparation of this book. It is not a comprehensive list of the thousands of research contributions which have been made.

*General Literature on Lasers and Laser Phenomena*

Tomiyasu, "The Laser Literature—An Annotated Guide," Plenum Publishing Corp., New York, 1968.

"Masers and Optical Pumping," a reprint volume published by The American Institute of Physics, New York, 1965, contains many of the original articles on lasers and nonlinear optics.

*Optics and Electromagnetic Theory*

Condon and Odishaw, "Handbook of Physics," McGraw-Hill Book Co., New York, 1958.

Stratton, "Electromagnetic Theory," McGraw-Hill Book Co., New York, 1941.

Landau and Lifshitz, "Electrodynamics of Continuous Media," Addison-Wesley Publishing Co., Reading, Mass., 1960.

Heitler, "The Quantum Theory of Radiation," Oxford University Press (Clarendon), 1954.

*Popular Reviews of Nonlinear Optics*

Terhune, "Nonlinear Optics," International Science and Technology (August 1964), p. 38.

Giordmaine, "Nonlinear Optics," *Sci. Am.*, **210** (4), 38 (April 1964).

*Static Nonlinear Effects*

Yariv, "Quantum Electronics," John Wiley & Sons, New York, 1967.

Condon and Odishaw, "Handbook of Physics," McGraw-Hill Book Co., New York, 1958.

Landau and Lifshitz, "Electrodynamics of Continuous Media," Addison-Wesley Publishing Co., Reading, Mass., 1960.

Jenkins and White, "Fundamentals of Physical Optics," McGraw-Hill Book Co., New York, 1937.

"American Institute of Physics Handbook," McGraw-Hill Book Co., New York, 1957.

*General Nonlinear Optics Theory*

Bloembergen, "Nonlinear Optics," Benjamin, Inc., New York, 1965.

Franken and Ward, "Optical Harmonics and Nonlinear Phenomena," *Rev. Mod. Phys.* **35** (1), 23 (January 1963).

Armstrong, Bloembergen, Ducuing, and Pershan, "Interactions between Light Waves in a Nonlinear Dielectric," *Phys. Rev.* **127** (6), 1918 (September 15, 1962).

Bloembergen and Pershan, "Light Waves at the Boundary of Nonlinear Media," *Phys. Rev.* **128** (2), 606 (October 15, 1962).

Pershan, "Nonlinear Optical Properties of Solids: Energy Considerations," *Phys. Rev.* **130** (3), 919 (May 1, 1963).

Ward, "Calculation of Nonlinear Optical Susceptibilities Using Diagrammatic Perturbation Theory," *Rev. Mod. Phys.* **37** (1), 1 (January 1965).

Yariv, "Quantum Electronics," John Wiley & Sons, New York, 1967.

Kelley *et al.*, "Physics of Quantum Electronics," McGraw-Hill Book Co., New York, 1965, 1966 (Proceedings of international conferences on quantum electronics).

Giordmaine, "Nonlinear Optics," *Physics Today* **22** (1), 38 (January 1969).


*Harmonic Generation*

Franken and Ward, "Optical Harmonics and Nonlinear Phenomena," *Rev. Mod. Phys.* **35** (1), 23 (January 1963).

Armstrong, Bloembergen, Ducuing, and Pershan, "Interactions between Light Waves in a Nonlinear Dielectric," *Phys. Rev.* **127** (6), 1918 (September 15, 1962).

Bloembergen and Pershan, "Light Waves at the Boundary of Nonlinear Media," *Phys. Rev.* **128** (2), 606 (October 15, 1962).

Terhune, Maker, and Savage, "Optical Harmonic Generation in Calcite," *Phys. Rev. Letters* **8** (10), 404 (May 15, 1962).


*Optical Mixing*

Armstrong, Bloembergen, Ducuing, and Pershan, "Interactions between Light Waves in a Nonlinear Dielectric," *Phys. Rev.* **127** (6), 1918 (September 15, 1962).

Bass, Franken, Hill, Peters, and Weinreich, "Optical Mixing," *Phys. Rev. Letters* **8** (1), 18 (January 1, 1962).


*Optical Rectification*

Bass, Franken, and Ward, *Phys. Rev.* **138** (2A), 534 (1965).

Bass, Franken, Ward, and Weinreich, "Optical Rectification," *Phys. Rev. Letters* **9** (11), 446 (December 11, 1962).


*Raman Scattering*

Eckhardt, Hellwarth, McClung, Schwarz, and Weiner, "Stimulated Raman Scattering from Organic Liquids," *Phys. Rev. Letters* **9** (11), 455 (December 1, 1962).

Zeiger, Tannenwald, Kern, and Herendeen, "Two-Step Raman Scattering in Nitrobenzene," *Phys. Rev. Letters* **11** (9), 419 (November 1, 1963).

Jones and Stoicheff, "Inverse Raman Spectra: Induced Absorption at Optical Frequencies," *Phys. Rev. Letters* **13** (22), 657 (November 30, 1964).

Platonenko and Khokhlov, "On the Mechanism of Operation of a Raman Laser," *Soviet Phys.—JETP* **19** (2), 378 (August 1964).

Fain and Yashchin, "On the Theory of Stimulated Combination (Raman) Radiation," *Soviet Phys.—JETP* **19** (2), 474 (August 1964).

Bloembergen and Shen, "Coupling between Vibrations and Light Waves in Raman Laser Media," *Phys. Rev. Letters* **12** (18), 504 (May 4, 1964).
Bloembergen and Shen, "Multimode Effects in Stimulated Raman Emission," *Phys. Rev. Letters* **13** (24), 720 (December 14, 1964).

*Brillouin Scattering*

Chiao, Townes, and Stoicheff, "Stimulated Brillouin Scattering and Coherent Generation of Intense Hypersonic Waves," *Phys. Rev. Letters* **12** (21), 592 (May 25, 1964).
Brewer and Rieckhoff, "Stimulated Brillouin Scattering in Liquids," *Phys. Rev. Letters* **13** (11), 334 (September 14, 1964).
Compton and Allison, "X Rays in Theory and Experiment," D. Van Nostrand Co., Princeton, New Jersey, 1935, pp. 231–233.
Slater, "Interaction of Waves in Crystals," *Rev. Mod. Phys.* **30** (1), 197 (January 1958).

*Plasma Generation*

Meyerand and Haught, "Gas Breakdown at Optical Frequencies," *Phys. Rev. Letters* **11** (9), 401 (November 1, 1963).
Minck, "Optical Frequency Electrical Discharges in Gases," *J. Appl. Phys.* **35**, 252 (January 1964).
Meyerand and Haught, "Optical-Energy Absorption and High-Density Plasma Production," *Phys. Rev. Letters*, **13** (1), 7 (July 6, 1964).
Ramsden and Davies, "Radiation Scattered from the Plasma Produced by a Focused Ruby Laser Beam," *Phys. Rev. Letters* **13** (7), 227 (August 17, 1964).
Archbold, Harper, and Hughes, "Time-Resolved Spectroscopy of Laser-Generated Microplasmas," *British J. Appl. Phys.* **15**, 1321 (1964).
Wright, "Theory of the Electrical Breakdown of Gases by Intense Pulses of Light," *Proc. Phys. Soc.* **84**, 41 (1964).
Gold and Bebb, "Theory of Multiphoton Ionization," *Phys. Rev. Letters* **14** (3), 60 (January 18, 1964).
Kroll, Ron, and Rostoker, "Optical Mixing as a Plasma Density Probe," *Phys. Rev. Letters* **13** (3), 83 (July 20, 1964).
Linlor, "Some Properties of Plasma Produced by Laser Giant Pulse," *Phys. Rev. Letters* **12** (14), 383 (April 6, 1964).
Bebb, "Theory of Three-Photon Ionization of the Alkali Atoms," *Phys. Rev.* **123** (1), 23 (January 5, 1967).
Platzman and Buchsbaum, "Light-Off-Light Scattering in a Plasma," *Phys. Rev. Letters* **12**, 573 (May 25, 1964).
Naiman, DeWolf, Goldblatt, and Schwartz, "Laser-Induced Prebreakdown and Breakdown Phenomena Observed in Cloud Chamber," *Phys. Rev.* **146** (1), 133 (June 3, 1966).

*Two-Photon Spectroscopy*

Kleinman, "Laser and Two-Photon Processes," *Phys. Rev.* **125** (1), 87 (January 1, 1962).
Braunstein, "Nonlinear Optical Effects," *Phys. Rev.* **125** (2), 475 (January 15, 1962).
Kaiser and Garrett, "Two-Photon Excitation in $CaF_2$ : $Eu^{2+}$," *Phys. Rev. Letters* **7** (6), 229 (September 15, 1961).

Abella, "Optical Double-Photon Absorption in Cesium Vapor," *Phys. Rev. Letters* **9** (11), 453 (December 1, 1962).

Hopfield, Worlock, and Park, "Two-Quantum Absorption Spectrum of KI," *Phys. Rev. Letters* **11** (9), 414 (November 1, 1963).

*Photon–Electron Scattering*

Milburn, "Electron Scattering by an Intense Polarized Photon Field," *Phys. Rev. Letters* **10** (3), 75 (February 1, 1963).

Fiocco and Thompson, "Thomson Scattering of Optical Radiation from an Electron Beam," *Phys. Rev. Letters* **10** (3), 89 (February 1, 1963).

Bartell, Roskos, and Thompson, "Reflection of Electrons by Standing Light Waves," *Phys. Rev.* **166** (5), 1505 (February 25, 1968).

*Intensity-Dependent Refractive Index*

Maker, Terhune, and Savage, "Intensity-Dependent Changes in the Refractive Index of Liquids," *Rev. Letters* **12** (18), 507 (May 4, 1964).

*Self-Focusing of Laser Beams*

Chiao, Garmire, and Townes, "Self-Trapping of Optical Beams," *Phys. Rev. Letters* **13** (15), 479 (October 12, 1964).

# INDEX